Albrecht on Pastures

The Albrecht Papers, Volume VI

by William A. Albrecht, Ph.D.
Edited by Charles Walters

About the Author

Dr. William A. Albrecht, the author of these papers, was chairman of the Department of Soils at the University of Missouri College of Agriculture, where he had been a member of the staff for 43 years. He held four degrees, A.B., B.S. in Agriculture, M.S. and Ph.D., from the University of Illinois. During a vivid and crowded career, he traveled widely and studied soils in the United States, Great Britain, on the European continent, and in Australia.

Born on a farm in central Illinois in an area of highly fertile soil typical of the cornbelt and educated in his native state, Dr. Albrecht grew up with an intense interest in the soil and all things agricultural. These were approached, however, through the avenues of the basic sciences and liberal arts and not primarily through applied practices and their economics.

Teaching experience after completing the liberal arts course, with some thought of the medical profession, as well as an assistantship in botany, gave an early vision of the interrelationships that enrich the facts acquired in various fields when viewed as part of a master design.

These experiences led him into additional undergraduate and graduate work, encouraged by scholarships and fellowships, until he received his doctor's degree in 1919. In the meantime, he joined the research and teaching staff at the University of Missouri.

Both as a writer and speaker, Dr. Albrecht served tirelessly as an interpreter of scientific truth to inquiring minds and persistently stressed the basic importance of understanding and working with nature by applying the natural method to all farming, crop production, livestock raising and soil improvement. He always had a specific focus on the effect of soil characteristics upon the mineral composition of plants and the effect of the mineral composition of plants on animal nutrition and subsequent human health.

Dr. Albrecht strove not to be an ivory tower pontificator trying to master and defeat nature, but to be a leader of true science and understand the wondrous ways of nature so we could harness them for the lasting benefit of all. A man of the soil, William A. Albrecht summed up his philosophy as such, "When wildlife demonstrates the soil as the foundation of its health and numbers, is man, the apex of the biotic pyramid, too far removed from the soil to recognize it as the foundation of his health via nutrition?"

Dr. Albrecht was a true student of the characteristics of soil and wasn't timid about his views—be they to a farmer in the field, an industry group or to a congressional subcommittee.

Respected and recognized by scientists and agricultural leaders from around the world, Dr. Albrecht retired in 1959 and passed from the scene in May 1974 as his 86th birthday approached.

About the Editor

Charles Walters was the founder and executive editor of *Acres U.S.A*, a magazine he started in 1971 to spread the word of eco-agriculture. A recognized leader in the field of raw materials-based economic research and sustainable food and farming systems, this confirmed maverick saw one of his missions as to rescue lost knowledge. Perhaps the most important were the papers of Dr. William A. Albrecht, whose low profile obscured decades of brilliant work in soil science. Albrecht's papers, which Walters rescued from the historical dustbin and published in an initial four volumes, continue to provide a rock-solid foundation for the scientific approach to organic farming. Additional volumes of Albrecht's papers were organized and edited by Walters for later publication—the result is shown here with this book. During his life, Walters penned thousands of article on the technologies of organic and sustainable agriculture and is the author of more than two dozen books (and co-author of several more), including *Eco-Farm: An Acres U.S.A. Primer, Weeds—Control Without Poisons, A Farmer's Guide to the Bottom Line, Dung Beetles, Mainline Farming for Century 21* and many more. Charles Walters generously shared his vision, energy and passion through his writing and public speaking for more than 35 years and made it his lifelong mission to save the family farm and give farmers an operating manual that they couldn't live without. The Albrecht Papers are an important part of this message. Charles Walters passed on in January 2009 at the age of 83.

About the Albrecht Papers

When the first volume of these papers was issued, no one could foresee the possibility of recovering and publishing all the papers of this great scientist. For this reason the organization of these papers has not followed Dr. Albrecht's work in a calendar sequence, meaning the order of study and investigation. Instead the papers have been organized into topic themes.

Here the papers have been grouped to best focus attention and allowed to reciprocate the values upon which all of Albrecht's work.

A Special Note

William A. Albrecht's biography is his work. A detailed recap of his personal life has never been accomplished largely because the published record of his scientific findings overshadow the quiet habits and even the extensive travels made necessary by his eminence. A chapter in *A Life in the Day of an Editor,* by the editor of this volume, enlarges the few geographical notes left on tape by Albrecht, a few paragraphs of which are repeated herein.

Albrecht
on Pastures

The Albrecht Papers, Volume VI

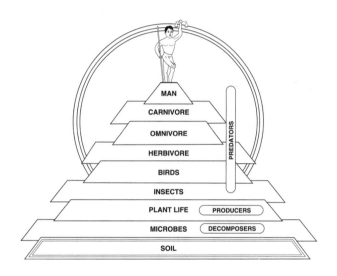

by William A. Albrecht, Ph.D.
Edited by Charles Walters

Acres U.S.A.
Austin, Texas

Albrecht on Pastures

Copyright © 2011 by Acres U.S.A.

Acres U.S.A.
P.O. Box 91299
Austin, Texas 78709 U.S.A.
(512) 892-4400 • fax (512) 892-4448
info@acresusa.com • www.acresusa.com

Printed in the United States of America

Publisher's Cataloging-in-Publication

Albrecht, William A., 1888-1974
Albrecht on pastures / William A. Albrecht., Austin, TX, ACRES U.S.A., 2011
    xiv, 250 pp., 23 cm.
    Includes Index
    Includes Bibliography
    ISBN 978-1-601730-25-1 (trade)

    1. Agriculture — pasture farming. 2. Crops — grassland.
    3. Forage — livestock feeding. 4. Soil fertility
    5. Conservation cropping. 6. Plants — nutrition.
    I. Albrecht, William A., 1888-1974 II. Title.

    SB299.A42 2011   633.2

**Dedicated to the memory
of John Whitaker, D.V.M.,**

*who taught a generation how to understand William A. Albrecht and
Albrecht's colleague, André Voisin, the champion of rotational grazing.*

From the Publisher

A large part of the Acres U.S.A. mission is to preserve and promote the wisdom of those who came before us. Prof. William Albrecht was such a visionary. A collection of his papers was the first publishing entry toward this mission, that book being *The Albrecht Papers*.

Charles Walters, our founder and longtime editor — and my father — sought out Dr. Albrecht not knowing what lessons were there to be learned. The name Albrecht appeared in journals around the world, yet officials at the University of Missouri where the retired professor kept an office discouraged a meeting citing his age, poor hearing, and the like. Charles Walters visited anyway. What came from these meetings, which soon grew into weekly sessions, was a mentor/student dialogue. Albrecht, ever the patient pedagogue, dispensed the logic, elegance and simplicity of his agricultural systems to an eager mind. And Charles Walters, the publisher and writer, picked up the charge and spread the timeless wisdom of William Albrecht around the world to a new generation of farmers and agronomists.

It's hard to say whether Dr. Albrecht's work would have found its way to light through the efforts of others or if without the republication of Albrecht's papers they would have remained just that, papers to eventually fall into the dustbin of history.

Four volumes of *The Albrecht Papers* eventually came forth. Each had a style and character of its own and each brought new lessons from the master soil scientist to life, but only the most disciplined students of the soil tended to seek out and study these dense works.

Late in his career, semi-retired and legally blind, Charles Walters undertook the Herculean task of reading and sorting the hundreds of remaining papers and articles in Albrecht's archives. He completed that task a few years before his death in 2009. What was left to accomplish was the monumental task of converting damaged and faded copies of articles, some 80 years old, into formats compatible with modern publishing and readable by all.

From file cabinets full of faded photocopies came forth several new volumes of *The Albrecht Papers*, each with a specific focus and theme. It is our goal to produce these works in a timely fashion. In your hands is the beautiful collaboration of the visionary research of Professor William Albrecht and the deft editorial eye of Charles Walters. We hope you enjoy this new creation of William Albrecht and Charles Walters.

— *Fred C. Walters*

Contents

Foreword

"Grass, the forgiveness of nature, her constant benediction," intoned the 19th-Century Kansas Senator, John J. Ingalls. Albrecht could only add his "Amen" when reminded of Ingalls' paean. "The cow," Albrecht said, "is the finest nutritionist on earth. She knows more than the greatest Ph.D. on a college staff." Albrecht echoes this sentiment in the papers assembled in this volume.

How did hay or grass perform when passed through the digestive tract of the test animal, be they rabbit, cow, horse, whatever? During his long career, Albrecht discerned a cause-effect response when producing high volume forage. The results he found in turn answered the dairy farmer's quest for knowledge on an equally perplexing question, just how much is high dissolved solids hay worth?

Morrison's *Feeds* and *Feeding* had no answers, Albrecht claimed, because laboratory tests are not biological tests. High relative feed values too often fail the fiber test, a test that condemns protein bypass, cattle cake and feeding schemes that seek to turn an herbivorous animal into a carnivore.

Pastures mean fiber. The absence of pastures often means disease. Albrecht's papers seem to anticipate some of the developments reported in the pages of the *Acres U.S.A.* magazine since he passed from the scene in 1974. The refractometer was little used in agriculture in his time, but Albrecht expected development of a test that preserved the validity of the biological procedure, yet yielded immediate and valid results.

One such testing system dries hay to a zero percent moisture, then hammers it into powder. That powder is dissolved in deionized or distilled water. Shaken and filtered, the material is then ready for a refractometer readout.

Dan Skow, D.V.M., has himself enlarged lessons and stair-stepped to a lofty real science status on the shoulders of giants. His refractometer calibration runs from zero to 80. It is the feed with a value of 50+ that is a guarantee of increased production.

Quality pastures and hay crops are not the given expected by farmers who row crop the best land and reserve fragile soils for pasture and hay.

All the lessons presented so far lay the foundation and backbone for cows at grass. One of Albrecht's correspondence associates was André Voisin, the author of rotation pastures and the book, *Soil, Grass and Cancer.* They had exchanged ideas, defined and launched investigations both at the University of Missouri and in France.

There are now two systems before the farmer and rancher. One relies on confinement feeding, what Albrecht called "the bovine concentration camp," now suggested by later day university studies that linked nutrition to disposal problems for industrial wastes—even chicken litter, cow manure, rendered animal wastes and protein bypass based on soy. Confinement best represents the industrial model imposed on a biological procedure. But turning herbivores into carnivores begged the biological question and left unanswered the animal health requirement.

The other system relies on grass, "the forgiveness of nature," as John J. Ingalls put it. Starting at the beginning of the last century, Albrecht and his colleagues proceeded to unravel the mysteries of grass, clover, alfalfa—all the legends, of course—and a bio-factory that suggested animal health. Farmers and scientists have been building on findings represented by those papers ever since.

Albrecht would have scoffed at industrial ads advising farmers to close down pastures for the purpose of row crop production. The farmer, it is argued, could grow more protein, yet the grower's chore is not to feed the feedlot, but to keep a bottom line that invites survival. Even in the 1930s and 1940s, Albrecht saw that the raw materials producer was being manipulated into the posture of a miner, one who sold his fertility without the benefit of a depletion allowance.

For their value-added status, pasture outdistances row crop production for reasons at once apparent when reading the lines (and between the lines) of the papers in this volume.

Of all the hay crops, grass represents nature's purest triumph. It avoids opening the soil to erosion, generally steps away from the conventional ignorance attending the use of pesticides, and cancels out many energy costs—all by animals simply grazing. If nitrogen and leaching remain as problems, the forgiveness of nature interdicts when reason is obeyed. The pastures Albrecht envisioned did not suggest high stocking rates and high nitrogen on confined areas. If all of agriculture offends nature, then it can be said that pastures are the least offenders.

During Albrecht's last few years in retirement, his correspondence included communications with André Voisin, the father of rotation pastures. Voisin's book, *Soil, Grass and Cancer* included Albrecht illustrations, and Albrecht gifted much of his library to this editor, *Soil, Grass and Cancer* included. It still invites study, as do these papers. The matter of pasture rotation is probably the one lesson universally accepted by graziers worldwide.

Results at Sanborn Field at the University of Missouri told Albrecht that some kind of legume is critical in the pasture mix, which in any case should include five or six species and wink at many weeds that seem to offend the psyche of mankind.

In our time, confinement of dairy cows and the resultant epizootics of Para-T bacteria or Johne's disease has become an issue. The offending organism reportedly survives the pasteurization process and accounts for irritable bowel syndrome, and Crohn's disease. Yet it has been established and recognized by dairy farmers that a lactating animal requires 3 or 3.5 percent of her body weight per head per day. A feeding system must furnish this amount, subtract 10 to 20 percent waste by trampling and cow platter contamination. This times the number of animals allows for computation of carrying capacity and the pasture payload has been computed.

Albrecht did not answer all the questions, but he posed many of them. A non-lactating animal can thrive on a rotation of a few days, perhaps as many as four. A lactating animal probably asks for a daily, and often a half day rotation.

On one point Albrecht remains in agreement with latter day scientists. Forage best transports nutrients to grazing animals and leaves in a cloud of dust dry feeds, fabricated feeds and all concoctions laced with industrial wastes that pretend to be micronutrients. Too many essential vitamins are quickly degraded in harvested feeds. This was established in feeding trials that served Albrecht as his biological tests. Poor pastures, starving animals, and resultant "infections" with brucellosis became a focal point of work of Albrecht and Francis M. Pottenger, M.D., researchers that became styled the miracle of the Ozarks. Indicated was the loss of nutrients whenever forage and feed endured a preservation process—grinding, silage, hay baling included.

Grass may be the forgiveness of nature, but grass is merely a metaphor for forage. Data contemporary to this publication date out of Effingham County Extension, University of Illinois, records results fairly consistent with the upper Midwest. These studies report a profit per acre of $80 for small grains (government deficiency payments included). Results for management intensive grazing include—dairy at $600 per acre; non-dairy cattle at $300 per acre, and sheep, somewhere between the last two numbers. Numbers become obsolete. Principles do not.

These papers ask many questions and stay on for the answers. With this book it is enough to invite eco-farmers to the intellectual feast Albrecht's writings always provide.

— Charles Walters, Editor

CHAPTER 1

Fertilize for Higher Feed Value

THE COW WAS one of the early fertilizer producers and distributors. Animal manures were put out by her as probably the first fertilizer. The nitrogen in her product was strongly emphasized for the nitrate salts collected from manures during the French Revolution for making gunpowder. The cow uses nitrogen fertilizers as the most demonstrative way of bringing to our attention the fertility shortage in the soil. She demonstrates the soil's need for fertility and gives suggestions on fertilizing it for more vegetative production every time she drops her voidings on a grassy area.

After the earlier observations of the cow in these activities, we began to talk about "manures and fertilizers." But today with fossil fuels and technologies as replacement of the horse for power, and with economic pressure on the soil for higher yields and higher monetary returns per acre, we do not use that binomial term. We omit the word "manure." We use, instead, only the term "fertilizer." Lately, we have not been observing the cow closely to study her performance of fertilizing in which she returns fertility to no small extent of what she takes away in the vegetation which she harvests. We have credited her with the capabilities in applying fertilizer to the fields for increased vegetative bulk per acre. We have, however, not noticed that she refuses to consume as feed that high yield of vegetation resulting from her application of her own fertilizer, namely her urine and her feces. That refusal exhibits itself, in most any pasture, by the spots of tall green grass growing taller and greener, while she eats the short grass around them still shorter. The cow has been most modest about her abilities as a soil manager via fertilizer treatments. By her refusal she has long been admitting that she produces and distributes a manuring combination which increases the vegetative yields of crops, but doesn't grow into them the nutritional quality making good feed. The producers and distributors of fertilizers of commerce suffer under a similar situation but the confessional exhibition of it is not given such prominence.

For legal purposes (not necessarily for biological services to growing plants and their services to growing animals), the term "fertilizer" has been defined as "Any substance containing nitrogen, phosphorus and potassium,* or any other element or compound recognized as essential or used for promoting plant growth, or altering plant composition, which is sold or used primarily for its plant nutrient content . . ."** On examining this definition, it is clear that the emphasis rests on (a) "promoting plant growth" and (b) "sold or used . . ." Little emphasis commonly goes to that part of the definition which says "altering plant composition." Our criterion of fertilizer values in soil treatments has been, almost singley, the increased plant growth or the greater mass of resulting vegetation. Emphasis on that criterion has simultaneously promoted fertilizer sales with the common reminder that the extra vegetative mass pays for the fertilizer costs and with a margin. In little or none of the sales promotion of fertilizers do we emphasize fertilizer use for its services in "altering plant composition" to give it higher value as animal feed. The placing of emphasis by careful choice and use of certain phraseologies, and the astute omission of others, seems to be exercised most adroitly by those selling fertilizers. Perhaps this merely emphasizes the shortage in research information of just what a fertilizer does under what conditions.

As another bit of phraseology for advantage or emphasis in the definition of fertilizers, there is the specification of the fertilizer contents, namely "Nitrogen, phosphorus and potassium and any other element or compound recognized as essential or used for promoting plant growth." The history of the technological developments giving major or minor amounts of available fertilizer materials reminds us that the phosphates were the first extensive commercial fertilizer. With the later availability of Chilean nitrate, the element nitrogen became prominent. Still later, the triumvirate of nitrogen, phosphorus, and potassium held main sway in the fertilizer market. At this date, nitrogen is in decided prominence again as the result of the chemical fixation of nitrogen with reportedly about 55 industrial plants fixing this fertilizer element in many chemical forms.

It is the making of a closer connection between the term "nitrogen" as a part of the definition of fertilizers, and the additional phrase there, namely

*Some fertilizer laws say phosphoric acid and potash.
**From the Missouri Fertilizer Law, 1953.

"altering the plant composition" with which the following discussion is concerned. It aims to relate the former as cause to the latter as effect. Then it aims also to include the cow's consideration of soil treatments, that is, the use of nitrogen to alter the plant composition as that quality of the herbage meets with the cow's approval of it as feed of high quality for growing young animals rather than for merely fattening castrated males.

Nitrogen is the Keystone in the Arch of Fertility Supporting Crop Production

It is significant to remind ourselves that before the advent of chemically fixed nitrogen as fertilizers, the soil's supply of nitrogen depended on that which was fixed biologically through the symbiosis between bacteria and the legume plant species, or through free-living bacteria in those soils naturally rich in calcium and other inorganic fertility, while also relatively high in organic matter. In that natural fertility situation, extra nitrogen came into the growth cycle via biological fixation to give more of it in the crops, more of it in turnover as decay in the soil, and more of it there in mobile nitrogen as ammonia, nitrite and nitrate forms. It was on those soils also where the ecological pattern included, not only more proteinaceous vegetation, but also more animal protein per acre in the many ruminant grazers ranging widely and subsisting as strictly herbivora.

We need to remind ourselves that it was, first, the presence of all the commonly considered, favorable physical and chemical conditions in the soil, and then, second, the biological fixation of the nitrogen which built up the proteins in the crops. The plant species with the complex physiologies represented by nitrogen fixation and high protein concentrations of such high values as feed for growing animals, demanded first that the inorganic fertility supplies be at high levels and in balanced ratios accordingly. Plants were then able to take nitrogen from the atmosphere.

Consideration of these unusual soil requisites for the natural production of high feed values, in terms of choice food proteins, raises the question whether our use of chemically-fixed nitrogen will not be disappointing in the quantity and quality of protein it encourages unless this product of the late fertilizer technology is used on soils of (a) high organic matter, and (b) high fertility in all the inorganic essentials except the nitrogen. Will fertilizer nitrogen serve best for growing higher feed values in forages save as (a) we choose crops of higher protein potential and (b) all other requisites of fertility in the soil have been supplied to the best of our knowledge.

"Crude Protein" Remains too Crude

In support of the above doubts, research studies offer accumulating chemical data and biochemical facts from bioassays using various animals, mainly rabbits, and even insects. The term "crude protein," as concentration, is no longer sufficiently critical as a criterion for classifying feeds, especially the feed values of what is included in the common term "proteins." Consequently the feed values have been more carefully and critically measured in terms of the array and the quantities of the different amino acids which the proteins contain according to the microbiological assay of their hydrolyzation products. This measurement of the different amino acids rather than the determination of the amounts of crude proteins is helpful, since now eight amino acids have been listed as essential for the human, ten for the laboratory rat, and specific numbers and amounts may soon be expected in reports for each kind of domestic or other animal.

Analyses of forages for their inorganic contents and for their amino acids, in relation to the fertilizer treatment and history of the management of the soil growing them, have given opportunity to examine both a non-legume and a legume forage grown under known soil treatments. Timothy hay in the former category was so examined for soil treatments with emphasis on applied nitrogen and trace elements. Red clover hay, in the latter category, from Sanborn Field was studied in relation to a wide variety of soil treatments and a long history of the soil management. These hays were analyzed for their inorganic compositions and their amino acid concentrations, and were then used in nutrition experiments with rabbits and crickets. The red clover was more critically studied than was the timothy hay.

Nitrogen Fertilizers on Timothy Do Not Make High Quality Proteins in its Hay

That timothy is one species of plant which apparently cannot be a feed of highest quality, even under nitrogen fertilization supplemented by much else (including the trace elements), was demonstrated by the poor gains in weights of weanling test rabbits fed on it. This fact was established under several tests, including the attempts to separate the effects of the individual trace elements as fertilizers. It was demonstrated most pronouncedly by the many deaths of rabbits from the heat in 1954, when they were fed on the timothy hay; but by no deaths when this feed was supplemented with other proteins fed the stock rabbits.

Weanling rabbits were fed wheat grain and timothy hay, only to have the high summer temperature kill many of them as the experiment progressed. The losses by death in the experiment were replaced at fortnightly intervals from the stock rabbits which were in the same environment but had not died while on a ration of the same wheat but this combined with green grass. At the close of the designed test period, and after losses amounting to over 70 per cent of the animals, the diet was modified by adding 10 grams of dried skim milk powder daily per rabbit. With the heat wave continuing and at temperatures higher than those of preceding periods, the extension of the test gave no fatalities from the heat after the introduction of the dried skim milk supplement into the ration.

Chemical analyses of the timothy hay, given in Table 1, suggest that the concentrations of many of the inorganic elements were lowered as the result of increased growth under the stimulation by the nitrogen fertilizer applied. This seems to be the case for most of the elements, save magnesium. The nitrogen fertilizer, as an addition to the basic fertilization with limestone, phosphates, and potash, failed to help this crop (rather it hindered it) in delivering higher concentrations of most of the inorganic essentials.

According to the biochemical data for the array of the amino acids in Table 2, the nitrogen fertilization increased the percentage of total nitrogen in the hay for the second and third increments of applied nitrogen but not, in general, for the first of it applied. The concentrations of the separate ten essential amino acids were also increased by the third increment of nitrogen, though not generally by the second. The first fertilizer increment served, in general, to reduce their concentrations. These facts suggest that under a heavy basic fertilization of all else, the first increment of nitrogen fertilizer increases the production of carbohydrate, or vegetative mass, and reduces the concentrations of the proteins in it though the total protein per acre is increased. It raises the carbohydrate-protein ratio. This occurs when the nitrogen is the major and seriously limiting deficiency in the fertility and the resulting forage gives a still wider nutritive ratio. However, even with its higher concentrations of the amino acids, the timothy hay was not a good feed for protection against the heat wave, unless supplemented by dried skim milk. We had not made the timothy hay a feed of high nutritional value.

Table 1

Inorganic Elements in Timothy

Treatment (Lbs. /A)	P %	Ca %	K %	Mg %	Na %	Mn p.p.m.	Fe p.p.m.	B* p.p.m.	Zn* p.p.m.	Co* p.p.m.	S p.p.m.
No nitrogen	.175	.280	1.43	.210	.07	147	355				1460
40# nitrogen**	.123	.217	1.18	.210	.045	147	364				1250
40# N + 30# N**	.129	.204	1.24	.268	.055	134	295				1270
40# N + 60# N**	.129	.187	1.16	.222	.045	119	419				1230
Mean	.139	.222	1.25	.227	.054	137	358				1302
40# N + 60# N**	.129	.187	1.16	.222	.045	119	419	3.7	10.4	.06	1230
40# N + 60# N** + B	.128	.235	1.11	.275	.055	134	345	5.5	4.8	.08	1280
40# N + 60# N** + Zn	.120	.192	.97	.262	.060	60	295	5.2	20.8	.02	1500
40# N + 60# N** + Mn	.136	.193	1.08	.157	.050	105	537	5.9	14.4	.08	1270
40# N + 60# N** + Co	.130	.221	1.03	.275	.050	105	352	6.2	12.4	.03	1410
40# N + 60# N** + Cu	.130	.238	1.08	.281	.050	105	337	6.0	22.4	.03	1420
40# N + 60# N** + all 5 trace elements	.152	.240	1.07	.238	.045	60	375	5.9	32.8	.03	1300
Mean	.132	.215	1.07	.250	.051	98	380	5.5	16.9	.05	1344

* Determined by spectrographic methods.
** Nitrogen fertilizer was applied in the form of solution.

Table 2

Ten Essential Amino Acids and Nitrogen in Timothy (Mgms/Gm Dry Matter)

Treatment (Lbs. /A)	Nitro-gen	Methio-nine	Tryp-tophane	Ly-sine	Threo-nine	Va-line	Leu-cine	Isoleu-cine	Histi-dine	Agri-nine	Phenyl-alanine	Total Amino Acids
No nitrogen	9.15	.50	2.48	.715	2.60	2.86	12.1	6.35	.812	2.86	2.48	33.76
40# nitrogen	8.84	.39	2.16	.894	2.00	2.64	9.0	5.11	.652	2.68	2.02	27.55
40# N + 30# N*	10.2	.35	2.24	1.20	2.40	2.76	11.5	5.58	.595	2.88	2.09	31.60
40# N + 60# N*	13.4	.52	2.90	1.65	2.80	3.69	14.6	7.12	.917	3.75	2.95	40.90
Mean	10.4	.44	2.44	1.11	2.45	2.99	11.8	6.04	.744	3.04	2.38	
40# N + 60# N*	13.4	.52	2.90	1.65	2.80	3.69	14.6	7.12	.917	3.75	2.95	40.90
40# N + 60# N* + B	14.7	.70	2.90	1.82	3.26	3.74	14.6	.05	.801	4.00	2.80	41.67
40# N + 60# N* + Zn	13.0	.56	2.86	1.58	3.04	3.23	13.2	7.13	.824	3.45	2.66	38.53
40# N + 60# N* + Mn	11.5	.57	3.39	1.40	2.80	3.48	13.5	7.20	.675	3.88	2.81	39.70
40# N + 60# N* + Co	13.4	.76	3.39	1.66	3.04	3.56	14.6	7.42	.893	3.88	2.86	42.06
40# N + 60# N* + Cu	12.1	.45	2.73	1.68	2.78	3.12	14.2	6.62	.670	2.55	2.53	37.33
40# N + 60# N* + all 5 trace elements	13.5	.72	3.61	1.84	3.06	3.59	13.6	7.31	.892	4.00	2.94	41.56
Mean	13.1	.61	3.11	1.66	2.97	3.49	14.0	7.12	.810	3.64	2.79	

*Nitrogen fertilizer was applied in the form of solution.

Red Clover Protein was a Much Superior Feed Value than Timothy Protein

That the red clover, as a legume hay, is far superior in feed quality than the timothy hay was shown clearly by a continuation of the rabbit feeding tests with timothy hay under the continuing high temperatures. This repeat of the previous trial used more of the stock rabbits which were given the same wheat and timothy hay again in the same ratios, save for some corn and other grains added to the wheat. The fatalities from the heat wave repeated themselves. After these had amounted to more than 30 percent, the red clover hay was substituted for the timothy hay. From the date of that change forward, no more heat fatalities occured under continued high temperatures. Here then was clear evidence of some factor or factors in the red clover of protective values equivalent to those in the dried skim-milk powder in terms of giving rabbit survival under the physiological stress of the continued high temperatures which had previously attained a maximum of 113° F.

Qualities of Protein in Red Clover Differ According to Fertility Differences in the Soil Growing it

These results were the occasion for the inorganic chemical analyses and the microbial assays of the amino acids of the red clover hay from three plots in the three-year rotation of corn, wheat, and clover, and from the eight plots of the four-year rotation of corn, oats, wheat and clover— all in the clover crop on Sanborn Field in 1954—in order to use these hays as the source of crude protein of a single legume plant species. These hays were used in constant total amounts of crude protein in making a ration for the rabbits. This was balanced as well as possible in all other nutritional factors in order to learn the differing qualities of the crude protein as determined by the fertility treatments of the soil growing this legume hay. The soil treatments of the 11 plots growing the clovers in 1954 are listed in Table 3. The inorganic chemical compositions of the hays by plots are listed in Table 4 for seven elements. The clover hays' contents of four nonessential amino acids are given in Table 5, while the concentrations of nine of the essential amino acids are listed in Table 6. The compositions of the feeds as modified to test the biological values of the proteins in the red clover hays are given in Table 7.

That the soil treatments made very significant differences in the feed value of the proteins in the red clover is shown by the wide variation in gains in the weights of the rabbits when the amounts of crude protein taken by them was a constant, save for the hay from one plot, No. 26, in the three-year rotation, as shown by the data in Table 8. In spite of the fact that the rabbits were consuming constant amounts of crude protein, that is, constant amounts of nitrogen, in the hay when all else was also held constant, yet the gains in weight per animal and the gains in weight per unit of the essential amino acids varied widely. The weight gains per

Table 3

*Soil Treatments and Rotations of the Plots on Which the
Red Clover was Grown*

Plot No.	Time	Rotation	Yearly Treatment
3	1940–1950	C-O-W-RC-T-T*	Fertilized for max. crops
	1950–1954	C-W-RC	Fertilized according to soil test + traces + residues
25	1940–1950	C-W-RC	6 tons of manure
	1950–1954	"	Same + nitrogen according to need
26	1940–1950	C-W-RC	9 tons of manure + 30# P_2O_5
	1950–1954	"	According to soil test + traces
27	1940–1950	C-W-RC	None
	1950–1954	"	None
28	1940–1950	C-W-RC	400# 4-12-4 + lime
	1950–1954	"	Maintaining sufficient level for Ca, P_2O_5 and K_2O
34	1940–1954	C-O-W-RC	6 tons of manure
35	1940–1954	C-O-W-RC	None
36	1940–1950	C-O-W-RC	200# 4-12-4 + lime
	1950–1954	"	According to soil test + traces + residues. Mg limestone used.
37	1940–1950	C-O-W-RC	200# of 4-12-4
	1950–1954	"	"
38	1940–1950	C-O-W-RC	200# of 4-12-4 + lime
	1950–1954	"	"
39	1940–1950	C-O-W-RC	200# of 4-12-4 + lime + residues
	1950–1954	"	Same as 36, except Ca-limestone instead of Mg-limestone.

*C-corn; O-oats; W-wheat; T-timothy; RC-red clover.

Table 4

Inorganic Elements in Red Clover Used for Bioassay

Plot No.	Phosphorus %	Calcium %	Potassium %	Magnesium %	Sodium %	Manganese p.p.m.	Iron p.p.m.
3	.097	.90	.98	.181	.027	20	85
25	.052	1.35	1.10	.251	.034	16	78
26	.033	1.05	1.65	.163	.033	87	67
27	.108	1.45	.98	.192	.029	86	240
28	.175	1.35	.83	.168	.034	12	180
34	.034	1.28	1.00	.261	.048	24	67
35	.038	1.20	.98	.220	.032	65	65
36	.137	.95	1.60	.185	.029	41	290
37	.157	1.15	.95	.266	.041	98	278
38	.137	.98	.85	.177	.034	107	138
39	.132	1.30	.70	.209	.033	41	135
Mean	.110	1.18	1.06	.207	.34	54	147

rabbit for the hays from different clover per plots and their different soil treatment varied from a low of 34 grams in four weeks for the clover on the plot, No. 25, given manure and supplemental nitrogen in the three-year rotation, to a high of 241 grams (more than 700 percent) for the clover grown on the plot, No. 36, formerly given lime and 4-12-4 fertilizer but later given magnesium limestone, crop residues, and fertilizers according to soil test suggestions, including the trace elements. The gains as grams per milligram of the nine essential amino acids in the feed varied from a low of 10.6 for the clover from plot No. 25, cited above, to a high of 77.9 (again more than 700 percent) for plot 39, in the four year rotation formerly given the same treatment as plot 36 and later duplicating that also save for a continuation of the treatment by calcium limestone rather than by the magnesium stone.

Table 5

Four Non-Essential Amino Acids in Red Clover
(Mgms/Gm Dry Matter)

Plot No.	Amino Acids				Total of Amino Acids
	Aspartic Acid	Glutamic Acid	Proline	Cystine	
3	11.4	10.7	2.33	1.43	25.86
25	9.37	11.5	2.48	1.28	24.63
26	12.0	11.6	2.42	2.02	28.04
27	11.1	13.1	3.60	1.41	29.21
28	11.1	12.4	2.87	1.46	27.83
34	7.75	12.1	2.80	1.77	24.42
35	9.12	11.4	2.90	1.06	24.48
36	14.6	14.3	3.10	1.14	33.14
37	12.9	11.4	3.33	.71	28.34
38	13.1	10.7	2.40	.78	26.98
39	14.9	14.4	2.92	.82	33.04
Mean	11.58	12.15	2.83	1.40	

Table 6

Nine Essential Amino Acids and Nitrogen in Red Clover (Mgm/Gm Dry Matter)

Plot No.	Nitrogen	Essential Amino Acids									Total Amino Acids
		Methio-nine	Lysine	Threo-nine	Valine	Leucine	Iso-leucine	Histi-dine	Argi-nine	Phenyl-alanine	
3	15.72	1.04	4.03	3.53	4.21	4.40	3.45	.97	9.38	3.28	34.29
25	16.72	1.44	5.15	4.64	5.26	6.08	3.91	1.12	8.57	4.37	40.54
26	14.70	1.08	4.65	4.07	4.02	5.40	3.94	1.35	7.77	5.88	38.16
27	17.91	1.15	5.35	4.79	6.37	7.50	4.74	1.40	10.30	4.75	46.35
28	18.53	1.22	5.80	4.39	5.71	5.75	4.14	1.37	8.87	5.10	42.35
34	17.55	1.33	4.38	4.23	5.59	5.45	3.95	1.15	8.80	3.87	38.75
35	18.18	1.33	5.40	4.61	6.54	6.40	4.74	1.42	9.90	3.97	44.31
36	19.01	1.55	6.50	4.93	6.12	7.00	5.03	1.70	11.30	5.04	49.17
37	15.44	1.48	5.60	4.92	6.59	6.75	5.61	1.50	11.30	5.38	49.13
38	16.70	1.50	5.40	4.77	5.79	5.74	4.16	1.40	9.07	5.36	43.19
39	20.91	1.25	5.65	4.73	6.54	6.28	5.05	1.66	10.20	6.51	47.87
Mean	17.4	1.31	5.26	4.51	5.70	6.07	4.43	1.37	9.59	4.86	

Table 7

Composition of Feed Used to Test the Biological Value of Protein in Red Clover Hay When Grown Under Different Soil Fertility Levels (Gms)

Ingredients	Plot No.								
	3	25	26*	34	35	36	37	38	39
Red Clover Hay	840	790	908	752	725	695	850	790	631
B. Complex 5%	50	50	50	50	50	50	50	50	50
Soybean Oil 3%	30	30	30	30	30	30	30	30	30
Codliver Oil 1%	10	10	10	10	10	10	10	10	10
Traces in Dextrose 1%	10	10	10	10	10	10	10	10	10
Total Minerals added	49.8	41.2	33.8	40.7	49.8	46.9	42.7	36.4	54.9
Dextrose added	10.2	68.8	-	107.3	125.2	158.1	7.3	73.6	214.1
Total (Gms)	1000	1000	1041.8	1000	1000	1000	1000	1000	1000
Nitrogen in hay (%)	1.57	1.67	1.47	1.75	1.82	1.90	1.54	1.67	2.09
Nitrogen in test diet (%)	1.31	1.31	1.26	1.31	1.31	1.31	1.31	1.31	1.31

* Instead of calculations based upon the nitrogen content of Plot 37, this should have been based upon Plot 26 due to its lower nitrogen in the hay. Due to this change in plan the nitrogen in the feed representing Plot 26 was relatively about 4% lower than for that off all other plots.

Table 8
Feed Consumed and Gain/Rabbit (Gms/Wk)

Experimental Period	Feed Consumed	Plot Numbers								
		3	25	26	34	35	36	37	38	39
1st	380	12	7	-2	30	39	30	9	-15	-2
2nd	520	-2	-22	28	74	55	50	18	43	57
3rd	555	25	26	50	50	67	51	95	69	75
4th	580	46	23	53	92	73	110	116	98	103
Total for 4 weeks	2,035	81	34	129	216	234	241	238	195	235
Percentage nitrogen in hay		1.57	1.67	1.47	1.75	1.82	1.90	1.54	1.67	2.09
Percentage nitrogen in feed		1.31	1.31	1.26	1.31	1.31	1.31	1.31	1.31	1.31
Nine essential amino acids (Mgms/Gm feed)		28.8	32.0	34.6	29.1	32.4	34.5	41.7	34.1	30.2
Gains (Gms/Mgm of nine essential amino acids)		28.1	10.6	37.3	74.3	72.4	70.0	57.1	57.3	77.9

A Big Market Remains for Fertilizers for Growing Higher Quality Proteins

The improvement in the protein quality of the feed which soil treatments can bring about depends, in no small measure in the first place, on the crop on which the nitrogen fertilizer is used. The effectiveness of nitrogen in this respect depends, in the second place, on the fertilization beforehand by the other nutrient essentials. Red clover grown in a rotation on well-fertilized soil converted its nitrogen into crude protein for much higher feed values of it than did the well-fertilized timothy, including increments of nitrogen as soil treatments. In the latter crop other treatments did not contribute as much to the protein quality as they did in the former. Even with our help and hope to improve the quality of the crude proteins they still remained too crude to the test animals.

It is highly significant to note that the bioassays of the red clover from Sanborn Field suggest that (a) the return of crop residues, (b) the use of calcium and magnesium limestones, and (c) the attempts to balance the soil fertility according to the soil tests with the addition of trace elements, were all essential contributors to the higher feeding values in the red clover for growing weanling rabbits. These factors in fertility under the crop of constant delivery of even crude protein as commonly measured were the variables to the extent of 700 percent in the nutritional quality of the forage grown by them.

In terms of these bioassays there is the suggestion that while fertilizing for higher feed values still be an extension of the market for fertilizers far beyond those areas which supply fertilizers for increased yields of bulk only, it will be, apparently, also a tremendous challenge to learn how we can fertilize the soil to grow the increase in protein quality accordingly.

CHAPTER 2

Microbiological Assays of Hays for Their Amino Acids According to Soil Types and Treatments Including Trace Elements

THE PLANT IS composed of carbohydrates, fats, nitrogenous compounds including proteins and vitamins, inorganic elements, and other substances possibly not classified in the above categories. The carbohydrates are produced by photosynthesis with the aid of a few inorganic elements such as magnesium in the chlorophyl, potassium for conversion of sugar to starch, and some of the minor elements, like manganese, for the transformation of sugar and starch to fats. The production of amino acids and protein is, however, not a photosynthetic but a biosynthetic process. This process probably depends on both the presence of, and the balance of, the supplies of inorganic elements in the plant as well as on the supply of carbohydrate. The quantities of these elements present are probably not the most important criterion of their service. Rather, the activities of the cationic and anionic constituents should probably be taken into account. It appears as if the role of these elements is mainly a catalytic one with only some of the elements actually becoming components of the protein molecule.

The primary objective of crop breeding has been that of increasing yields as measured by the quantity of material produced. Very little thought has gone to the quality of the crop in relation to the purposes it serves. This objective has resulted, in many cases, in the adoption of crops that give increased yields in carbohydrates. Yet, the provision of the carbohydrate content of rations for farm animals is a relatively simple matter. The serious problem in feeding farm animals is one of getting sufficient protein of proper quality even when we resort to the purchase of protein concentrates to balance the carbohydrates as energy in the diet.

Proteins are not commonly measured directly but only indirectly. This is done by oxidizing the organic substances slowly in the presence of sulfuric acid to retain the nitrogen. The total nitrogen in the ignited remains is determined and then multiplied by a numerical factor with the result considered as the protein. The inadequacy of such a generalized method of measuring the protein is readily evident. When it is now known that certain of the constituents of protein, namely, the essential amino acids, must be present in the animal's diet, and when there must be a definite ratio between those essential ones in the diet for maximum efficiency in the utilization of foods, such general measures of protein by ignition and simple factor multiplication are of no service in specificity.

Chemical studies which make use of the complete destruction of the organic parts of the plant for an analysis of the remaining inorganic elements have been of some value in the qualitative analysis of the plant. But they have not enabled us to determine the combination of these inorganics with the organics produced by biosynthesis. We obtain the concentration of inorganic elements instead of their activity and function within the plant in terms of organic output.

Biological assays have been used more recently in the evaluation of feeds in relation to the fertility of the soils growing them. Little correlation has been established between the results as animal growth and the ash analyses or the protein contents as measured by the total nitrogen method. However, sufficient work has been done in feeding experiments to show that those soils generally considered poor from a viewpoint of yield production and those generally considered good show the same respective order in that crops from poor soils result in poor and diseased animals, while crops from good soils generally result in good healthy animals. It has frequently been shown that differences between fertile and nonfertile soils may be greatly magnified when measured in terms of animal growth.

This bio-assay method of evaluation, while useful along with the ash analyses of the crops, tells us nothing about different combinations of the inorganics with the organics, nor about the nature of the plant composition when any particular element in the soil is there in a deficient concentration. Therefore, we may well look to the synthetic nitrogenous compounds as good indicators of the plant processes involving cation metabolism and thereby indicating the services by the fertility of the soil. In the following study the vegetative plant parts were microbiologically assayed for their contents of nine amino acids in order to correlate, if possible, the concentration of these with the soil treatments, particularly some trace elements.

Experimental Procedures

Crops, Soil Types, and Treatments

Korean lespedeza and alfalfa were the two crops assayed for their amino acids by a microbiological method as outlined by Stokes, Gunness, Dwyer, and Caswell with appropriate modifications.

The lespedeza, previously assayed chemically and biologically in feeding trials, was grown on the outlying experiment fields representing the five different soil types of Missouri. They were the Eldon sandy loam, Lintonia fine sandy loam, Putnam silt loam, Grundy silt loam, and Clarksville gravelly loam. These five soil types represent five distinctly different soil areas as regards parent material, age, topography, and vegetation. The soil treatments included lime and phosphorus on all these soils. In addition, potassium was also applied on the Eldon and Putnam soils.

The alfalfa was grown on the Putnam soil at the Missouri University farms at Columbia. Again all the plots were limed to insure a stand of the legume. In addition, phosphorus and potassium were applied as major elements. Across these plots there were applied the trace elements boron and manganese. This procedure aimed to correlate the differences found in the amino acid contents of the alfalfa with the application of the major elements and the minor elements as supplements.

Chemical Methods

The carbon determination was made by the common combustion train method and other elements were determined according to methods outlined by the Association of Official Agricultural Chemists.

Microbiological Methods

The amino acids assayed were valine, leucine, arginine, histidine, threonine, tryptophane, lysine, isoleucine, and methionine. The microbiological method begins with the hydrolysis of the plant proteins by the use of 20 ml of 5 N sodium hydroxide per gram of dried plant material for the determination of the tryptophane and 10 ml of 10% hydrochloric acid per gram of plant material for all other amino acids. A basal medium composed of amino acids, vitamins, and salts was used, and as each successive amino acid was assayed the corresponding amino acid was in turn deleted from the medium. The pure amino acid was then added to a set of standard tubes in increasing known concentrations. The protein sample was diluted by trial and error until the concentration of the amino acid in the protein sample approximated that in the standard tubes. Water was then added to the tubes to bring the volume to 5 ml and 5 ml of the appropriate basal media were added to each tube to bring the total volume to 10 ml. Each tube was then sterilized and inoculated with the proper lactic acid bacteria specific for the amino acid being assayed. After inoculation the tubes were incubated for 48 hours and then read by means of a photometer to measure the turbidity resulting from the growth or multiplication of the microorganisms in the clear media. The value (2—the log of the galvanometer reading) was plotted on the ordinate of a graph with the concentration on the abscissa. Curves were drawn for the standard and for the unknown so that the concentration of the amino acid in the unknown plant sample could be determined by reading from the unknown curve to the standard curve and then to the abscissa.

Of the lespedeza, the entire portion (that normally taken for hay) was used, while of the alfalfa, only the growing tip was taken. The reason for using the growing tip of the alfalfa was the belief that elemental deficiencies would manifest themselves first in the highly proteinaceous tip of the plant where growth represents the maximum production of protein.

Results of the Chemical Analyses & Microbiological Assays

Lespedeza Hays from Different Soil Types

The chemical analyses of the lespedeza hays suggested an order of decreasing fertility of these five soils which differed from the order established by their reputations and behaviors in crop production. The concentrations of the essential elements were higher in some cases in the hays produced on the supposedly poor soils, than in the hays produced on the supposedly more fertile soils. The percentages of nitrogen, phosphorus, and lignin increased with the soil treatments. The carbon contents of these plants were relatively constant but the carbon-nitrogen ratios varied considerably due to the variation of the nitrogen concentration from a high of 2.6% to a low of 1.9%.

The concentrations of amino acids in the lespedeza hays were extremely variable as shown in Table 1. Little, if any, direct correlation could be

Table 1

Concentrations of the Essential Amino Acids in the Lespedeza Hay Grown on the Different Soil Types With and Without Soil Treatment (Per Cent of Dry Weight).

Soil	Treatment	Valine %	Leucine %	Arginine %	Histidine %	Threonine %	Trypto-phane %	Lysine %	Isoleu-cine %	Methio-nine %
Eldon	Treated	0.895	1.055	0.646	0.375	0.632	0.294	0.992	2.08	0.092
	Non-treated	0.917	0.978	0.429	0.343	0.569	0.205	0.943	1.67	0.086
Lintonia	Treated	0.922	1.038	0.451	0.342	0.625	0.279	0.872	1.63	0.077
	Non-treated	0.780	1.014	0.329	0.306	0.544	0.181	0.878	1.68	0.077
Putnam	Treated	1.023	1.280	0.716	0.362	0.639	0.244	0.894	1.89	0.084
	Non-treated	0.986	1.289	0.563	0.503	0.606	0.227	1.007	2.26	0.080
Grundy	Treated	1.010	1.174	0.627	0.367	0.690	0.196	0.797	2.00	0.079
	Non-treated	1.137	1.460	0.456	0.381	0.671	0.195	0.938	2.00	0.082
Clarksville	Treated	0.853	1.025	0.340	0.389	0.585	0.258	0.930	1.59	0.076
	Non-treated	0.941	1.199	0.367	0.356	0.557	0.215	0.870	1.38	0.074

found with differences in soil types in that the supposedly better soils did not give the higher concentrations nor the poorer soils the lower concentrations. The concentration of the amino acids increased, in general, as the percentage of nitrogen increased but there is no direct relationship. This would indicate that possibly varying amounts of the nitrogen are combined in some of the stable ring structures or in some of the amino acids which have not been determined. This again points out the limited value of the determination of the total nitrogen and suggests the possibility of drawing erroneous conclusions when basing nutritive status upon the values for the total nitrogen alone.

The concentrations of tryptophane and threonine were apparently increased in the forage from each soil type as a result of soil treatment. The arginine concentration was higher in the hays from the treated soils in all cases except on the Clarksville, while the concentrations of the other amino acids follow no definite pattern.

A comparison of these amino acid values of the hays with the results of the biological assays of them as given by feeding tests, shows no direct quantitative agreement. The hays giving the better gains and efficiencies when fed to rabbits do not necessarily contain the higher concentrations of any of the amino acids. Instead, however, there seems to be a greater uniformity and possibly a better balance of the separate amino acids with these smaller variations among them.

Required Levels of Amino Acids for Animal Nutrition

If we compare the percentage concentrations of these amino acids with the values suggested by W. C. Rose for the concentrations necessary in the diet of the young rat for optimum growth, and if we assume these hays to be the ration, then the assayed acids, except tryptophane and methionine, were sufficient and in excess. The former was a borderline case. The latter varied considerably and was present in only about one-seventh of the amount required. These values and this observation seem valid. They are borne out by the fact that by supplementing legume hay with 0.1% of the 1-methionine, Marais and Smuts were able to increase the nitrogen utilization by young animals by as much as 30%. This certainly points to the need for supplementing the feeds—even good, green, nutritious legumes—with a protein supplement especially high in tryptophane and methionine in order to obtain optimum results.

Amino Acid Nitrogen as Part of the Total Nitrogen

When the concentrations of the amino acids were calculated as their nitrogen represented certain percentages of the total nitrogen, it was found that the nitrogen of valine, leucine, histidine, threonine, lysine, and methionine as percentage of the total nitrogen was actually decreased by soil treatment while that nitrogen for arginine and tryptophane was increased as shown in Table 2. The concentrations of the acids when expressed as per cent of the total dry weight were increased by soil treatments in most cases, as explained previously, but a smaller portion of the total nitrogen was combined in the amino acids assayed. Such facts seem rather peculiar since these amino nitrogen compounds are essential for growth and since results from feeding tests with rabbits with these same hays gave huge increases in growth as a result of soil treatment over those not treated. Evidently there is present in these treated forages some undetermined nitrogenous "growth" substance, or substances, which allows more efficient utilization of these hays than of hays from the untreated soil.

Alfalfa Hay on Treated Soils Including Trace Elements

The carbon content of the alfalfa, like that of the lespedeza, was also relatively constant. There was a rather high nitrogen content, but it varied only from 4.65% to 4.95%. The same general variation in the amino acid content of the alfalfa was found as for the amino acids in the lespedeza. The data are shown in Table 3.

The interesting observation here was that variation in the amino acid contents of these plants, which were all grown on the same soil type, was due entirely to the relatively small amount of inorganic elements applied to the soil. Probably the most significant variations were derived from the application of manganese and boron. In these two instances the greatest increase in the concentrations of most of the amino acids resulted from the manganese treatment. The exact nature of the action of these minor elements in biosynthesis is not known. It is possible, however, that their action is a catalytic one and that the proper conditions must be present for maximum efficiency. Variations resulted from the application of phosphorus and potassium, and of a mixture of phosphorus and potassium with minor elements. There was little correlation between these soil treatments and amino acid concentrations. It should be pointed out, however, that

Table 2

Nitrogen in Amino Acids as Percentage of Total Nitrogen.

Soil	Treatment	Valine	Leucine	Arginine	Histi-dine	Threo-nine	Trypto-phane	Lysine	Isoleu-cine	Methio-nine	% N as amino acids
Eldon	Treated	4.45	4.70	8.63	4.22	3.08	1.67	7.89	9.21	0.359	44.3
	Non-treated	5.73	5.47	7.21	4.84	3.48	1.47	9.42	9.29	0.425	47.4
Lintonia	Treated	4.74	4.78	6.24	3.98	3.14	1.64	7.18	7.47	0.310	39.5
	Non-treated	4.57	5.31	5.19	4.06	3.11	1.22	8.23	7.47	0.353	40.7
Putnam	Treated	4.67	5.23	8.77	3.74	2.85	1.28	6.52	7.69	0.307	40.4
	Non-treated	4.85	5.69	7.45	5.60	2.92	1.29	7.94	9.93	0.331	46.7
Grundy	Treated	4.97	5.15	8.26	4.09	3.31	1.10	6.13	8.75	0.304	42.2
	Non-treated	5.98	6.86	6.47	4.55	3.47	1.19	7.93	9.44	0.363	46.2
Clarksville	Treated	4.67	5.02	4.98	4.80	3.12	1.61	8.14	7.72	0.327	40.3
	Non-treated	5.85	6.67	6.13	5.00	3.38	1.52	8.65	7.66	0.362	45.4

Table 3

Concentrations of Amino Acids in Dry Alfalfa Leaves According to Soil Treatment of Calcium, Phosphorus, and Potassium, and of these plus Manganese and Boron as Supplements (Per Cent of Dry Weight).

Soil Treatment	Valine %	Leucine %	Arginine %	Histi- dine %	Threo- nine %	Trypto- phane %	Lysine %	Isoleu- cine %	Methio- nine %
Calcium	2.19	4.37	0.380	0.654	0.862	0.546	1.57	2.64	0.100
Calcium + manganese	2.40	4.89	0.434	0.807	0.954	0.640	2.12	3.63	0.242
Calcium + boron	2.13	5.55	0.418	0.726	1.071	0.856	2.13	4.09	0.173
Calcium + phosphorus	2.34	5.34	0.406	0.790	1.099	0.516	1.86	3.63	0.170
Calcium + phosphorus + manganese	2.33	4.90	0.459	0.828	1.078	0.546	1.89	3.76	0.198
Calcium + phos + boron	2.03	4.72	0.434	0.815	1.078	0.500	1.87	3.63	0.176
Calcium + potassium	1.97	5.14	0.450	0.840	1.033	0.770	1.72	3.75	0.190
Calcium + potassium + manganese	2.10	4.93	0.399	0.828	1.016	0.770	1.72	3.75	0.198
Calcium + potassium + boron	2.11	4.68	0.373	0.685	0.822	0.530	1.70	3.50	0.196
Calcium + phosphorus + potassium	2.19	4.88	0.427	0.740	1.071	0.460	1.53	3.02	0.159
Calcium + phosphorus + potassium + manganese	2.07	4.86	0.426	0.745	1.046	0.600	1.56	3.60	0.275
Calcium + phosphorus + potassium + boron	2.00	4.97	0.399	0.745	1.363	—	1.50	3.20	0.178

since superphosphate and potassium fertilizers contain impurities in the form of some of the minor elements, it is possible that part of the variation in the results here, as well as in practical agriculture, may be attributed to these small quantities of trace elements applied when superphosphate and muriate of potash are used.

Discussion

Since plants differ only slightly in their energy values on ignition, and since the energy or the carbohydrate contents of plants are of little concern in practical feeding of farm animals, it seems that the time is ripe for some objective by the agronomists other than that of merely increasing the vegetative bulk of our crops. In the development of new hybrids, we now recognize their increased rate of depletion of the soil fertility and in many cases their lesser nutritive value per unit than for the former smaller-yielding crops they have displaced. Even in purchasing feeds we need to give more attention to the fertility of the soil upon which the crop was grown. Varieties as such are not nutritional guarantees per se. We can not safely say that alfalfa, merely because it is alfalfa, is superior in nutritional value to lespedeza or other varieties. That the nutritional values, like those in the amino acids, depend on the fertility of the soil is brought out rather forcefully by data of these studies. The results as determined by this microbiological method indicate that variations may be had in forage feeds suffering from a deficient supply of fertility elements even when that deficiency has not developed to the extent of manifesting external deficiency symptoms in the plant.

The results obtained showed that the single plant species grown on different soil types was not constant in amino acid contents and, consequently, that variations in the quality as well as the quantity of protein occurred as a result of small applications of calcium, phosphorus, and potassium on the different Missouri soils. The fact that there was no correlation between the inorganics or ash elements in the hay and the concentration of any particular amino acids, simply points out the extremely complicated mechanism of soil and plant relationship in biosynthesis. This lack of correlation also points to the extreme difficulties which arise in attempting to separate the effects of any one element in protein synthesis since the matter of synthesis concerns a balance of all the elements. A deficiency of any one, if severe enough, will disrupt the entire physiology of the plant.

Summary

1. The percentages of the essential amino acids contained in the lespedeza hays varied as a result of differences in the soil types and of differences in the soil fertility of any type as a result of soil treatment.

2. The increased concentration of the amino acids in the crop does not necessarily mean that a larger share of the crop's total nitrogen is in the amino acid form. While soil treatments are giving higher concentrations of the amino acids there may also be an increase in the total nitrogen in the forage resulting from soil treatment.

3. Variations in the concentration of the amino acids present in the alfalfa were shown to be due to manganese, boron, phosphorus, and potassium but the minor elements manganese and boron gave the greatest increase without appreciably altering the total nitrogen.

4. It seems readily possible to improve the quality as well as the quantity of the protein produced per acre by the relatively small application and wise choice of inorganic nutrients applied to the soil.

5. The uniformity and balance of the inorganic constituents reflect themselves more in providing a relative uniformity in the amino acids than in increasing any of the individual amino acids.

6. The extremely complex nature of the soil-plant relationship renders untenable the belief in any simple evaluation of forages and other feeds by means of ordinary chemical ash analysis, and suggests that this whole subject of soil fertility in relation to both photosynthesis and biosynthesis by the crop demands further study if nutritous foods are to be continuously produced.

CHAPTER 3

How Good is Grassland Farming?

IN HIS ARTICLE entitled "Is Grassland Farming Bunk?" Mr. Gale Evans of Indiana points out that, in the humid eastern half of the United States, grassland farming is not a good means by which to build up, or even maintain, the fertility of the soil. Much has been said recently to carry the belief that it is. Mr. Evans cites his practices of such a scheme of farming to point out the error of such belief.

Grass May be Soil Cover Anywhere, But it Becomes Nutritious Forage Only as the Soil Fertility Makes it So

Mr. Evans reports the common fallacy in believing that the planting of certain crops, and that certain rotations of them, build up the fertility or productivity of the soil. This fallacy is often implied when folks speak of "Prairie Soils" and "Forest Soils" and in that classification of the soils they imply that the former is more fertile than the latter because the grass made it more so than the forest trees did.

This belief is usually supported by citing the fact that the virgin soils which grew the shorter grasses originally also grew herds of bison and today have herds of cattle growing themselves successfully in that area. Also, since soils which originally grew the taller prairie grasses were taken over to be good soils on which to grow wheat and corn, a particular virtue has been attributed to grass crops as though this crop made those soils fertile.

It is also recognized that soils under grass do not erode seriously, since the dense mat of such vegetative cover absorbs the destructive and erosive impact of the falling raindrops. The grass crop has therefore been considered a Godsend to prevent erosion of the soil and at the same time to be good feed for the grazing animal. Poetic language has extolled its many virtues supposedly pointing in these directions.

Little thought is given to the defective logic in giving the same grass crop these two virtues, namely, (a) good cover against erosion and (b) good feed for grazing animals, when two widely different levels of soil fertility under the grass may be the differing causes of these two values and thereby, really, two different kinds of grass crops may be involved.

Basically, Mr. Evans is citing this fallacy: namely, that the simple introduction and the growth of the grass crop on the humid, highly developed, less fertile soils of Eastern United States did not make this crop a great feed. Nor did these build up the fertility of the soil under his experience. Grass established its qualities and reputation as good feed for buffalo and cattle on the Great Plains because the more fertile soil out there was responsible.

Grass came east as seed but did not bring that fertile soil along when it traveled in that direction.

Therefore the grass growing on the humid soils is not the same quality as the grass growing on the Plains. Therein two different physiological performances by the grasses were involved, and therein is the origin of the fallacious belief that the grass made the virgin Plains land fertile and will therefore build up the soil in Indiana for Mr. Evans if he uses grassland farming merely as a cropping scheme expected to build up the soil.

Plants Don't Play Santa Claus

It was an advertisement for tobacco which once said repeatedly "Nature in the raw is seldom mild." Accordingly, plants cannot be expected to be philanthropists making soils fertile for animals and for us. Instead, plants are taking from the soil all they can to grow the most reproductive potential for themselves.

So when grasses covered the mid-continent and served so well in the growing of young grazing animals and in keeping older ones surviving, it was because those soils were growing protein-rich and mineral-rich feed constituents in the grasses as well as offering carbohydrates in them.

In finding so much more complete nutritional service by the grass, namely, the protein and mineral supplements to the carbohydrates grown right into the feed, we are prone to consider the plant species as the cause of the excellent nutrition of the animal. We fail to see the high fertility of the soil under the grass as the real cause for this complete feed service to the animals.

Such high fertility was the result of the particular climatic setting of moderate to low rainfall which prohibits the trees requiring water more regularly, if not more abundantly, but allows survival of the intermittently growing crop of grass which accommodates itself to periodic summer shortages of water and is not extinguished by drought. Such a drier climatic setting which eliminates forests but grows grasses, does not wash out the fertility of the soil when the rainfall scarcely exceeds the evaporation.

Virgin soils so slightly developed are therefore fertile; they grow wild legumes; and they build themselves up in organic matter. Consequently they produce protein-rich mineral-rich vegetation by which the so called "grass" or "prairie" soils obtained their reputation as fertile soils.

It was in consequence of the fortunate fertility construction that grass has erroneously gotten the reputation that it builds a less fertile soil into a more fertile one. Growing the grass is not making the soil fertile. The fertile soil is making the grass grow as a better feed, even though grass will grow itself as soil cover on much less fertile soil where it will have less quality in its services in animal nutrition. Because grass grows, that is no proof that it is delivering nutrition.

Mr. Evans is testifying in a similar way to the fact that, contrary to common belief, the rotation of the crop does not build up the soil. Rather the farmer does so by bringing fertility in from some other sources such as limestone for calcium and magnesium; rock phosphate, or that treated with acid for the phosphorus ammonium and nitrate compound for nitrogen; sulfate compounds for sulfur; and manures, green residues and other organic materials for all the fertility value these can add to the soils.

These soil treatments will all serve to feed a single crop which may well be grown continuously if these soil treatments feed it better than they feed any other crop, including weeds. Unfortunately, we have long been turning our crops out to rustle for themselves. We are not yet able to feed any one crop well enough in one place to grow it continuously, and are, therefore, not able to feed a series of crops in succession or in a rotation on the same soil. Mr. Evans is learning to keep no more than two major crops in rotation fed well enough to reduce the troubles with fungi, insects, etc., as hindrance to his keeping his crops more healthy.

At the same time that those crops are building protection for themselves in their own proteins, they are delivering more of these within their forages for better nutrition, better protection against disease and better reproduction of the animals feeding on them, as Mr. Evans' experience testifies.

It is these organic compounds, namely proteins (not carbohydrates and fats), which (a) carry life or growth, (b) protect against diseases as invasions by foreign proteins, and (c) reproduce the species. They are so complex in chemical make-up that plants producing them are now suggesting, according to recent facts, that they must have organic compounds as starter fertilizers from which to synthesize or create them.

Plants on wholly inorganic fertilizers can scarcely be expected to create all the organic chemical complexities of these elaborate proteins during a single growing season unless they are fed by the soil with some complex organic compounds like those put back in manures, for example.

"Organic" Fertility is Gradually Being Considered Along with the "Ash" Fertility

In depending on grass because of its erroneously assigned reputation, Mr. Evans found himself led astray by grassland propaganda which emphasizes grass but disregards the soil fertility under it. However, when he looked to the soil and managed its fertility, he found that grassland farming without attention to the soil was bunk as any crop farming is that expects mere faith in the species rather than both faith and work in the fertility of the soil to give the larger, more nutritious crop yields.

Now, that, for one hundred acres of crop land Mr. Evans has brought in annually 100 tons of dry matter in the 200 tons of manure resulting from the purchased feed; that tobacco stems high in potassium come on to the farm as litter; and that mineral fertilizers come in also for sheet composting in the fields; he finds that all this organic matter is coming in to build up the soil in that respect and is supplemented by inorganic fertility as a means of growing more of the organic fertility into the soil.

All of this really puts "life" into the soil. It starts more decomposition of the reserve minerals still left in the soil or of those applied. It gives more creative activities within the soil now expressing themselves in the tons of poultry protein in the more healthy birds Mr. Evans is harvesting and marketing as human food of possibly higher nutritional values.

Mr. Evans is simply telling us that when we propagandize the crop we must make certain that we consider the soil by the fertility of which alone that crop's physiological activities can do for us what we expect from its creative, or biosynthetic, services in terms of proteins that grow animals and man and keep them healthy.

Crops don't make the soil. Only soils of high fertility will feed the crops to feed us.

To believe that merely scattering grass seed is grassland farming, represents the bunk which Mr. Evans is emphasizing. It is bunk to believe that any kind of crop farming will succeed unless we feed the crop well by means of fertile soils suited or balanced so as to provide the crop's need for its own complete nutrition.

CHAPTER 4

Pasture Grasses Need Additional Nutrients to Furnish Livestock Ample Protein Supply

JUST AS GRASS is feed for the cow so she can give us proteins as well as fat and water in her milk, so must fertilizers be fed to the grasses so they can make the parts of the proteins which the cow passes on to us.

Plants make energy feeds readily; but they make protein feeds with difficulty. Carbohydrates as calorie- giving foods are synthesized, or put together, from the simple elements in air and water. The plant does this mainly through the energy effects of sunshine while but little is taken from the soil. But when it comes to making the proteins, even the plants seem to have trouble in supplementing their mineral needs from the soil for this function. They have been struggling to get proteins for themselves much as we have, then, in getting protein supplements for feeding our dairy cows and other livestock.

Since cows and other animals can get proteins only according as their feeds pass to them the constituent portions of proteins (called amino acids); and since plants, as we know for legumes, cannot make proteins on many soils without soil treatments, we can look at fertilizers as if they were protein and mineral supplements for the growing grass and thereby better as such for the cow.

One can put fertilizer on the pasture either in the early spring or in the late summer. Late summer is a good time to put fertilizer on the pasture to make future grass better. This is a good practice where the summer is apt to be dry and followed by autumn rains. Renovation of an old pasture by discing, fertilizing, and reseeding can well be done at that season when the grass is dormant. Relatively complete fertilizers according to soil tests, will build their nutrient elements into the grass at this time when this crop is not being pushed by the increasing sunshine power (as is true in the spring) to use all this to make more plant bulk, mainly carbohydrates.

Instead, with the shortening of the daylight period, the carbohydrates are manufactured into plant proteins and other storage compounds for reproduction. These will be carried over for rapid growth during the next spring when the sunshine intensity and length of day are both increasing to build plant bulk rapidly. Fall-grown grasses are, then, protein-rich feed for the cow so she too can build up a protein reserve on which to go into the winter.

Spring treatment as a top dressing is also good practice. The addition of nitrogen deserves attention then. Phosphorus, however, is taken more slowly. It is better when put *into* rather than *on top of* the soil. It should be down where the roots find it later in the moist soil. This does not move downward on its own solubility as the nitrogen does. It must be put down. Grass is just like corn and other summer crops. Its roots cannot feed in the dried surface soil.

CHAPTER 5

Better Pastures Depend on Soil Fertility

THE INCREASED DEMANDS for food under wartime labor shortages on the farm are bringing us face to face with the problem of wisest management of our lands for their direct delivery of milk and meat through animal harvests of their crops. The use of more pasture crops, and the more efficient use of lands already in pasture, suggest themselves as wise means of greater output of food with minimum labor. But many so-called "permanent" pastures go to weeds so extensively that much labor and machinery are demanded in mowing them. In addition their animal-carrying capacity is often so low that their service in terms of food production scarcely warrants their consideration as significant war crop producers when in contrast a few tilled acres in other crops could be so much more effective in animal output.

But since Missouri—as is true of many other States—is already a grain-importing State, the arable acres should go for grain production. Consequently the grass and forage needs must be met by attention to those acreages already devoted to herbage crops. Shifting these acres out of pasture and into row crops is not good agricultural policy as the first World War told us. That their animal output per acre can be improved; that their labor, costs in terms of the fight against weeds can be reduced; and that their season of grazing service can be extended—all by means of supplying some soil fertility—has not been widely recognized. The permanent timothy plots and the timothy crops in rotation on Sanborn Field bear testimony that these are possibilities that can be realized.

Soil Treatments Push Up Grass and Hay Yields

Lands in pasture have seldom been given much help toward greater production by means of soil treatments such as limestone, phosphate, or other fertilizers. Pastures have been a kind of stepchild on the list of different crop uses of fields of the farm. They have usually been disregarded when manure was to be hauled out. Manure has been considered more valuable on lands going to grain crops. Data from Sanborn Field at Columbia, however, testify that manure used on the permanent timothy plots has given the highest returns per acre and per ton of manure applied on this old experimental field when it was put on the grass crop.

Where timothy has been the continuous crop now for more than 50 years, the annual application of six tons of manure has netted a ton and a quarter of hay as the increase. Where three tons of manure have been used on timothy following clover in a six-year rotation this barnyard fertilizer has also given a ton and a quarter of hay as its return. Where this light application of manure was combined with phosphate, this application of soil fertility has given just about a ton and a half of extra timothy hay as the return on the investment put into the soil for a common pasture crop. When pastures are the areas left over after acreages for intensified tillage are listed, and they can be put into intensified production of food via milk and meat through soil treatment, there is every reason to give thought to fertilizing the pastures now when fertilizer use pays so well and when food is needed so badly.

More Fertile Pastures Save Labor of Weed Mowing

Much has been said about the need to mow pastures as a means of eliminating the weeds. It has been contended that cutting the weeds is necessary in order to keep them from going to seed and spreading their infestation. We have given a little thought to the fact that the incidence of weeds in a pasture is evidence of declining soil fertility, which if pushed up to a higher level by lime and other fertilizers, would grow grasses so well that weeds would find no place.

This fact is again well illustrated by the plots on Sanborn Field. On the continuous timothy plots where manure has been applied annually there are no weeds. It needs mowing only in making hay. It is a fine mat of densely-growing timothy plants. Where no fertility is returned and the timothy is left to maintain its pseudo-permanence through efforts wholly its own, there has been a gradually increasing incidence of weeds. After a period of about six to eight years in sod the land must be plowed and reseeded to this crop. This has been the behavior of this grass plot during 55 years of its history. It testifies that as a permanent grass plot there is permanence only in the adjoining plot where manure is returned as soil treatment. There is no permanence when left without attention to its fertility. When ample fertility grows a good grass crop there are no weeds to mow. Where the fertility is not returned weeds require mowing.

During this past year the timothy plot without manure demonstrated nicely how permanent pastures like this one, neglected as to fertilizer treatments, shift over to become fields of broom sedge (*Andropogon virginicus*). It was eight years ago when these timothy plots were last plowed and reseeded as a means of maintaining them under the more nearly comparable crop conditions required in careful experimental studies. Weeds of various kinds have taken their prominence in the succession of them on the untreated plot. It was not until fall, however, after the weed collection had been cut for hay during the summer, that this plot became a complete stand of broom sedge. It was as late as November that this weed crop blossomed and set its seed crop. Broom sedge demonstrates its final and complete possession now as a perennial weed crop on this soil where many other weed crops have had their short stay and then passed out as the exhaustion of the available fertility starved them out. Here now mowing might seem necessary, but of what profit or service would it be?

Different Degrees of Soil Fertility Invite Different Weed Infestations

That the infestation by broom sedge during this year was confined so thoroughly to this untreated permanent timothy plot, while all the other plots on the field were not taken by this weed suggests that the level of soil fertility is a factor in making the land susceptible to a particular weed infestation. Different weed crops represent their own different chemical compositions as the studies by A. W. Klemme demonstrate. As such, each weed crop demands delivery of soil fertility in different chemical combinations of kind and amount. Broom sedge as a crop suggests that it can find enough fertility in the soil after a series of other weeds have taken their share and then found themselves starved out. As the last to date in the succession here it made 3,700 pounds of vegetation per acre even after the summer cutting for hay. Apparently as a perennial crop with its root stock sending up new shoots each year, it could get a foothold only in this plot remaining long unplowed. It apparently cannot establish itself in the other plots of the field, all of which are in rotations and do not have periods of absence of plowing longer than three years.

In the six-year rotation where the timothy was the crop in 1943, the untreated plot was also devoid of timothy. The treated plots had a good timothy crop. In place of the broom sedge, however, the weed that had taken the untreated plot completely as early as August was not broom sedge. It was tickle grass (*Aristida*). As an annual this weed crop made its entrance on this cultivated soil that had been reduced in its fertility through continued crop removal and with no soil treatments as fertility return. On the uncultivated continuous timothy plot just across the roadway, however, the weed infestation was a perennial crop of broom sedge. Differences in the rotation and in the amount of plowing brought different weed crops to demonstrate difference in these infestations.

More Soil Fertility Means Immunity to Weeds

Exhaustion of the soil fertility to make the land susceptible to weed infestation is clearly pointed out by these two cases when all the other plots on the field were immune. There is little danger that the seeds from these weed crops will infest the rest of the field, when surely the seeds that infested these susceptible plots last year fell likewise on all the other plots but failed to grow up as weeds. Mowing of these weedy plots now in order to eliminate the danger of infesting the rest of the field is thus unnecessary, when it has already been demonstrated that the other plots grow other crops so completely that these weeds find no place in the keen competition for the nutrients of the soil.

Higher levels of soil fertility, brought on and maintained by the use of manure and fertilizer, are thus demonstrating that they give larger yields of the desirable crops to which the fields are planted. In addition, the soil treatment eliminates the weeds and saves the trouble and expense of mowing them. It controls the weeds, not by fighting them, but by better nourishment of the paying crops that eliminate them. In terms of labor saved by eliminating weeds, soil treatments are good economy, particularly when mowing machines are rationed and costly, and when summer labor is scarce.

More Soil Fertility on Pastures Lengthens the Grazing Season

Dairy farmers, in particular, have often reported the pronounced economies that could be effected by extending the fall-grazing season by only one month. This extension is considered so significant because it eliminates one month of wholly-barn feeding. Little has been said for the possibilities in the much better feeding value of the green feed that is rich in hidden values. One extra month on such a feed may be extremely significant as a reducer of the time period on dry feeds when disease incidence is high, and the reproductive load is approaching its peak.

Soil treatments on Sanborn Field demonstrated again this past year that increased soil fertility prolongs the growing period of the grass crop and thus extends the grazing season. Timothy plots given manure, given less manure and limestone, and given manure, limestone and super-phosphate were still green in late November. Extended growth of the crop by giving it some soil fertility by which it can keep on growing suggests that we have possibly been labeling the crops as "short-seasoned" when in reality they have been merely starved by poor soils. A small amount of limestone, phosphate or other fertilizer to keep a crop growing longer appears as a simple method of extending the grazing season.

More Soil Fertility Means More Nutritious Feed, Better Animal Health and More Meat per Acre

In shifting to pasture crops as they are to provide a larger share of farm production there is the serious danger that we shall let increased woodiness and lower feeding value of the forages creep in unnoticed. Grain crops record the declining soil fertility by lowered yields of grain per acre. Grains are more nearly of constant chemical composition. Hence if the soil is too poor to provide generously the nutrients going into the grain, there simply is less grain. Forages measured as tons per acre do not reflect differences in soil fertility so accurately. Plants on soil too poor to make seeds still make tons of forage. But such forage that wouldn't take seed can't deliver for animal sustenance many of the nourishments that go from the forage to the seed in its formation and serve in the nutrition of animals.

As the fertility of the soil declines, there come into the pasture those crops which the animals refuse to eat and which are commonly call weeds. Animal choice testifies to the plant's chemical composition. Broom sedge is not taken by cattle. Sedge still makes tons per acre. So does tickle grass.

But the disregard of them by the animals testifies that it is not the tonnage that serves in making meat. Mowing the weeds to eliminate them brings no change in the fertility within the soil.

As the fertility declines there is a change in composition within the same crop. As the soil delivers less of nitrogen, phosphorus, calcium and other plant nutrients then the crop is made more of carbon, hydrogen, and oxygen, or of air and water that make for woodiness. It is not so much an increase in woodiness as a decrease in what the plant manufactures inside of its woody structure. It is these different substances synthesized within the plants that are particularly nutritious. It is these that can be lacking even when tonnage harvest seem ample. This is the phase that may be the deception in our going to more forage crops unless we provide extra soil fertility.

Meat production is first a growth performance and later a fattening process. Growth is a matter of getting from the plants about a dozen chemical elements that the plant must first get from the soil. Fattening depends on the delivery of carbon, hydrogen and oxygen, coming from the air and water. But fattening cannot occur unless soil-given nutrients first make the growth of body frame. For growth and reproduction of the animals, soil treatments are of distinct value. The effects of lime and phosphate on the soil as they reach through the crops to the animals have been demonstrated recently. Lespedeza hay grown in 1941 on soil given phosphate only was 30 per cent more efficient, and that given both lime and phosphate was 67 per cent more efficient in promoting lamb gains than lespedeza hay grown without these fertility applications. Potency of males as breeders is also connected with the fertility of the soil. All of these effects add up to make pastures more efficient, and not hazardous, if we will see that the plants are fed with fertilizers before we can expect the pastures to feed the livestock.

Pastures like all other fields cannot be disregarded with reference to manures and other fertilizers and yet cropped continually without loss in their yielding power. The soil is dynamic. It is delivering the elements of fertility that serve in plant growth and likewise in animal growth. This delivery is not perpetual. It is dwindling and with its decreased offerings have come changes in the kinds and qualities of the pasture plants. The incidence of weeds and the refusal of the animals to eat them have been the dumb beasts' plea for our attention to the soils. They have been calling for some help toward their better growth and more efficient reproduction by means of limestone, phosphate and other fertilizers as soil treatments. War necessities, priorities, labor shortages, and other impositions are bringing

NO TREATMENT   SOIL TREATMENT

Not only growth improvement results when the hays are grown on fertilized soils but also better animal physiology as shown by better bones.

us to realize that grasses are no escape from diligent farming that is based on fertile soils.

Pasture Farming Can be a Paying Kind of Farming

Farming has higher earning power on the investment as the yields per acre go up. These go up as the soil has more fertility from which they are synthesized. Limestone and other fertilizers should be added to the pasture soils just as to soils in other crops. Such treatments will improve the tonnage of grass crops per acre with no increased cost of harvest by the animals that do so as pay for the privilege with more animal gain.

Soil treatments lessen the costs of attention to weeds by eliminating them, they extend the grazing season well into the fall; and they shift the composition of the herbage toward improvement of animal health, nutrition, and more animal gain per acre. Pasture grasses can be pushed up most effectively and also animal harvest therefrom increased with the soil treatments. As a war help, pastures are an unusual opportunity for more food production. But for its realization we must look to the fertility of the soil.

Animal choice testifies to the differences in chemical composition of the crop when hogging down of corn takes first the areas given soil treatments. Farm of Cliff Long, Warrensburg, Missouri. (Photo by County Agent Virgil Burke.)

CHAPTER 6

Cater to Cows' Tastes by Soil Treatments on Pastures

WHILE WE ARE emphasizing the use of more grass as cover for the soil against erosion, we are subconsciously including more cows as the means of converting that herbage into human food values. It is, of course, high time to practice more conservation of the soil, but is also necessary to design any enlarged program of grass production so that it will cater to the cows' tastes as well as cover Nature's nakedness.

It was Prof. R.J. Pool of Nebraska who pointed out that "Nature is not a nudist by choice, but man has robbed her of the means by which she can grow cover for her modesty." That remark suggests that crop removal and no return of fertility bring on its depletion and expose bare soils which would otherwise be naturally covered quickly. It might also suggest that soils too poor to grow their cover quickly are growing a vegetation that is probably too poor in quality to serve as animal feed.

During any campaign for more grass it is fitting to ask the question whether we are catering to the cows' tastes when thin, infertile, eroding lands are put to grass of any kind merely for the sake of cover. Shall we not emphasize the function of the grass as feed for the cow more than as blanket protection against falling rain-drops and as miniature dams against water running in rivulets? Isn't the production of highly nutritious forage the primary function of putting land into pasture; and isn't the saving of the soil the secondary one when by proper soil treatments the primary function can be carried out and the secondary one can be accomplished simultaneously without extra cost?

When Pastures "Run Out"

Whenever a part of the farm has some topographic features to make the use of larger machinery difficult, or if its productivity is making economically questionable the yields of seed crops under tillage, we are prone to consider putting it down to grass. If a fairly respectable sward results in the early years of such a program, it is usually not very long before the pasture is "taken by the weeds" or considered to have "run out."

When such conditions result, we are inclined to search for some new grass crop that will give tonnage production again where the bluegrass or preceding combination of pasture plants could no longer survive. When weeds take over the pasture, we often consider mowing as a good help to restore grass by eliminating the weeds as competitors for soil moisture along about mid-summer.

That the cows' taste enters into this weed problem in pastures because the declining soil fertility gives lowered feed quality in the pasture crops may, at first thought, seem far-fetched. But what is a weed in the pasture, after all? Isn't it a kind of plant which the cow will not eat? Should we not think of it as one that can make only woody bulk refused by the cow because the soil isn't fertile enough to grow the more nutritious herbage which the cow takes regularly. In Nature it is the forests or woody crops that occupy the soils which are thinnest and not so productive when cleared and put under cultivation. Can't we believe that the cow is allowing the weeds to grow because they are not producing anything worthy of her consumption for its nutritive value? If she refuses to mow the weeds, her seeming fastidious taste is telling us that our running the steel mowing machine over the pasture is not striking at the crux of the problem of getting good grass as she judges it.

When pastures go to weeds, nature is merely adjusting the crops by bringing in those that can make their growth on less of the soilborne nutrients that are essential for animals and plants. Weeds are made more extensively of air and water which are fuels rather than real nutrition. The mowing machine cuts down the plants the cow refuses to eat. But it adds no new supplies of lime, phosphorus, nitrogen, potassium or other essential elements that would encourage the dominance of plants like blue grass and legumes using these soilborne nutrients in manufacturing the higher feed values the cow prefers as she demonstrates in her preferential grazings. Pasture renovation calls for other machines in addition to the mower. It calls for the manure spreader or the lime and fertilizer distributors, as the cow's taste tells us.

More soil fertility where six tons of manure were applied annually on continuous corn (upper photo) grew winter protection against erosion, while no soil fertility returned to the companion plot left the soil naked (lower photo). Condition in early May, Sanborn Field, Columbia, Missouri. (Photo Missouri Agricultural Experiment Station.)

Catering to the Cows' Tastes Guides Soil Building Wisely

The grazing animals have so often demonstrated their discriminating tastes that most any farmer can report startling observations of the choice by cattle between forages according to differences in the fertility of the soils growing them. Usually the animal takes, first, in the humid regions, the forage where the soil was limed, given phosphate, manured or made more fertile in some way. Observations of such were reported by E. M. Poirot of Golden City, Mo., when his beef cattle grazed first the small parts of the barley field where in drilling out the corners he doubled over and thereby applied 200 pounds of mixed fertilizer in contrast to only the 100 pounds put on the rest of the field.

Choices by the cow and other animals are apparently not so often the cases where only one nutrient element is applied. They are probably more often cases of the better balance of several elements through which the feed output by the crop fits better into the animal physiology that is registering its needs by way of the animal's discriminating taste. Almost everyone is familiar with pasture scenes where there are bunches of the tall green grass resulting from the nitrogen dropped there in urine from the livestock. The cow disregards these bunches to let them grow taller while she eats the short grass around them still shorter. That the cow recognizes the lower feeding value of grass with this excessive and unbalanced fertilizer treatment, is suggested by the failure of experimental rabbits to do well when fed grass similarly fertilized, while their litter mates did well on the same species of grass not fertilized with liberal amounts of this one element alone.

When the shelled grains of corn from a series of plots producing different amounts of sweet clover turned under as nitrogenous green manure ahead of this crop were put into separate compartments of the self-feeder for hogs, the animals exercised an interesting selection. With 100 pounds of grain in each compartment representing one particular plot of the series fertilized to give more clover growth turned under, the relative rate of corn consumption was measured. This consumption rate decreased as the extra soil treatments gave greater amounts of sweet clover turned under as green manure. The corn from the plot with no soil treatment and therefore little sweet clover turned under was most highly preferred. However, when red clover was the green manure, their relative selections were reversed. Their consumption rate was highest where soil treatments gave the largest amounts of this green manure turned under. These differences demonstrate variable responses by the animals' taste according to the nature of the nitrogenous fertilizer turned under for the corn. Seemingly one is a balance and the other an unbalance for them.

Here are the suggestions that plants grown on the better soils in terms of general balance of fertility are chosen by animals because of greater nutritional service from them. When plants as forages, or even their seeds, are not taken by animals, there is the suggestion that the soil is of low or of unbalanced fertility from which the vegetative growth cannot compound those substances of most nourishing services. Catering to the cow's taste by treating the soils to grow grass crops according to her likes may be a kind of soil building under the guidance of a highly refined animal assay rather than under that of the laboratory chemist. Taking the cow's tastes into consideration would seemingly lead us to a better pastoral agriculture, when the measure of it is taken in terms of meat and milk.

Fertile Soils Immune to Weeds

We have not yet come generally to believe that by feeding lime and other fertilizers into our soils we make them healthy soil bodies to the same degree as we believe for our own bodies the old adage "that to be well fed is to be healthy." Yet, when it is almost axiomatic that there is much immunity to infectious disease in our good health might we not consider that good health of soil through fertility may represent in it an immunity to invasion or "infection" by weeds? For if soils are well-stocked with all the necessary elements of fertility, they will encourage rapid growth of dense cover of the planted, desirable grasses with which weeds cannot compete. On such soils the fertility diet for the crop is one that encourages the plants which are given to synthesizing the complex compounds of highly nutritional value and thereby those that satisfy the supposed idiosyncrasies of the cow's tastes. Does this not suggest that an insufficient soil fertility, or poor diet, for crops gives weeds and thereby a poor diet for the cow in terms of her choice and her output of food products for us?

Sanborn Field, with its 55 years of cropping history at the Missouri Experiment Station, recently demonstrated the fact that high fertility in the soil may well be considered an immunity to weeds, while soil exhaustion may be manifested by an increasing susceptibility. Two plots in this old field have been in timothy continuously since the start of the field in 1888. One is given six tons of manure annually. The adjoining plot gets no return of any fertility. Both have hay taken off every year.

While the timothy under regular manure treatment grows well and excludes the weeds, the plot with no manure starts off with a good stand after each occasional reseeding following plowing. But it is gradually taken by weeds. Consequently, it demands plowing and reseeding of both plots about every 6–8 years in the attempt to keep them more nearly comparable as timothy stands.

This shift during about 6 years from timothy to weeds in this plot which is cropped continuously but given no return of fertility or no manure, suggests a greater susceptibility to weed infestation. This was demonstrated forcefully by the advent of broom sedge (*Andropogon virginicus*) a few years ago when this plot was approaching the eighth year following the last plowing and reseeding. The weedy hay crop of a ton and a quarter taken in June was followed by a broom sedge crop of 3200 pounds per acre in late October. These combined annual weed productions were a tonnage yield greater than that of fine timothy hay in July on the adjoining

Cattle grazed out the barley first where in turning around with the grain drill the regular application rate of fertilizer was doubled. (Photo by E. M. Poirot, Golden City, Missouri.)

manured plot. Yet had the cow been permitted to exercise her choice she would have classified the latter crop of lesser tonnage as good feed and the former of greater acre yield as weeds and not as feed.

Only this one plot amongst the 40 or more plots with all the different fertility treatments on this experiment field had become susceptible to an infestation by broom sedge. Can we say that the winged seeds that started this weed crop were dropped on this plot alone and not over the border-lines that separate it from the plots adjoining. Can we imagine that the light feathery seeds of the "Old Man's Beard," as this weed is often called, were not scattered over the entire field at the same time they were seeded on this plot?

Here is encouragement to believe that infestation by weeds may be viewed as a case of our neglect of the fertility of the soil rather than the visitation of a great evil upon us. The applications of manure, lime, and other fertilizers may well be considered as a prevention of weeds at the same time that they are helps in providing more and better animal feeds.

Consider the Cow While Considering the Crop

Unfortunately, the tonnage yield per acre has been the prominent criterion that has guided our search for, and selection of, forage and grass crops. When one crop has gone down in its yields we have brought in other crops, mainly because they gave more pounds or tons per acre. Such has been the story of the introduction of some forage legumes, originally quite foreign. Consideration has not gone to the crop's capacity to cater to the cow whose taste is concerned and whose service as a provider of milk or meat as well as a regular multiplier of her own kind are at stake. She is, after all, the final criterion that must come in to determine what services will be rendered by the crop that must be consumed by her and thereby converted into human food products.

The grass crop is good mechanical help against erosion in terms of its services as soil cover. But as a cover it cannot be laid on the land except as the fertility of the soil grows it there. This same soil fertility determines how serviceable grass will be as a feed for the cow that converts it into cash. It is primarily this latter function for which grass is grown. It is essential, thereby, that the applications of soil fertility for growing more grass as soil cover be guided toward making better feed of it by catering to the cow's taste through soil treatments. For the dairy cow there may well be considered the same philosophy of feeding as was suggested for the hog by Professor J. M. Evvard when he said, "If you will give the pig a chance, he will make a hog of himself in less time than you will." The cow, too, may classify under this category if we cater to her tastes.

CHAPTER 7

Building Soils
for Better Herds

WE NOW RECOGNIZE our farm animals as very able connoisseurs of the quality of their feeds.

When we accept the self feeder, we admit that the pig will make a hog of himself quicker than we will. We can appreciate the unusual ability of our grazing cattle to assay the feed values of their forages more accurately than we can when we observe that they let the tall grass on the spot of their droppings grow taller, while they eat the short grass around it shorter. Then, too, they are always trying to get the grass on the other side of the fence, provided that other side of the fence is out on the highway or on the railroad right-of-way. They prefer such places because there the soil fertility has not been exhausted by excessive cropping. If, in grazing, they can call the nutritional qualities so accurately in their "dumb" way of telling us, shall we not come to see that by giving attention to better treatments of our soil with limestone and other fertilizers, we can very probably build the soils for better herds?

Virgin Prairie Soils Suggest
Patterns of Proper Fertility

"But just how shall we know what treatment should go on our soils in order to grow better cattle," you may already be asking.

Perhaps you have already had some answers to that question. Suppose we look at the fertility outlay in our virgin soils or what the soils contained in the days before they were tilled and cropped. Perhaps some of them can offer suggestions.

Declining soil fertility because of decreasing return of organic matter has brought in the Mesquite where once there was a cattleman's paradise. (Upper photo 1903, lower photo 1943.) (Photo courtesy of U.S. Forest Service.)

You will recall that westward from the Mississippi River, or even from some distance east of it, there were the prairie grasses on the prairie soils. These lands were not growing herds of domestic cattle when the pioneer first ventured into that region.

The prairies were, however, producing those big-boned, well-muscled hulks of animal flesh of similar feeding habits, namely the bison. These animals were meat for the Indians. They were entirely grass fed. They were grown without any purchased protein supplements and, apparently, must have found their native forage of the proper nutritive ratio. One needs to ask why buffaloes had chosen, and stayed on, a particular soil area. These meat producers wandered north and south over almost the same soil belt as that where we now grow hard wheat. This is the crop producing grain which is recognized as good food, particularly in whole wheat bread, and from which the young growth makes good pastures for lots of Herefords today.

There on the prairies was the soil that was naturally built for better herds. There were the soil contents as nutrients that can be put through the modern chemical tests and bio-assays to give us a good pattern soil for beef production. There was the fertility condition toward which we can build up the fertility of the other soils by the necessary soil treatments. That is the kind of soil that we want to duplicate when we use lime, nitrogen, phosphate, potash, magnesium, and the less prominent, or "trace," elements as treatments to improve our soils.

Prairie soils were fertile in calcium or lime. Streaks of this were found down in these soils within a few feet of the surface. They contained reserves of minerals supplying other nutrients. Those soils were acid enough to break down and make these nutrients available to plants. Legumes were growing naturally and thereby providing feeds that were growing young animals rather than merely fattening old ones. Soils were not as acid as those farther east. On these more eastern soils today we know that the difficulty in growing the mineral-rich, protein-producing crops for more efficient feeds is due to the absence of calcium and other fertility that went out when the high rainfall and heavy cropping put acidity there in exchange for them.

The prairie soils were well supplied with nitrogen, because when once it was taken from the air by the legumes to construct their vegetative bulk and then either grazed off by the bison or left in the grass, this fertility element went back in humus form on the death of both. The soils' contents of phosphorus were assembled from the rock minerals by the searching plant roots. This element was left in bountiful quantities in the surface soil layer in the organic and highly available form by this cycle of growth, death and decay in place.

Large amounts of potash were also active in soils so heavily stocked with organic matter going down so deeply. Being in regions of moderate rainfalls and periodic droughts, and being traversed by rivers hauling unweathered mineral sediments eastward from the arid region to be blown as deposits over them, these soils had regular additions of inorganic nutrients. Surely then, the chances were running high here that even the "trace" elements, like manganese, cobalt, copper, iodine and others would be present in the soil and the vegetation. At any rate, all the nutrients were there in the quantities and in the territories sufficient for the bison. They are the fertility pattern toward which we can build our other soils today by our soil treatments.

Forest Soils Present Soil Problems for Livestock Production

While the prairie soils of our mid-continent still support herds today, they do so less effectively according to the proportion in which we are depleting the soil fertility by moving it off the farm in the grain and the livestock. Our declining soil fertility has been pushing beef cattle westward. This movement, some might say, is due to economics. But when the "hard" wheat, or high-protein wheat, is also marching westward, it may not be erroneous to see the animals as the protein manufacturing part of agriculture, going west when the protein producing plants go out there, because the needs for lime and other fertilizers for them on our other soils are constantly growing more serious.

Perhaps you will grant that the exhaustion of soil fertility caused the movement of the big beef cattle market from the East to Chicago years ago and its movement lately from there to Kansas City. When we remember that the soils of the eastern and southeastern United States were originally low in their fertility because this was washed out by high rainfalls, we can readily understand why our beef animals can reproduce and be grown more efficiently after those soils are treated with limestone and other fertilizers to correct the fertility deficiencies. Such treatments make better herds. These result because soil treatments make the once-forested soils and their forages more nearly like those of the original prairies, where protein production as well as carbohydrate production was more readily possible.

If the soils were originally forested, they were then already relatively low in fertility even before we cleared them. They were providing potash, which helps the plants use the air and rain water to build carbohydrates, that is sugar, starch, and cellulose to make their wood. But potash is rather badly out of balance with other less prevalent elements for the plant diet that would enable the plants to make protein and big seed crops. The diet for the vegetation was already too low in calcium or lime, which is the soil requisite that we in the eastern United States associate with protein production, for example, by legumes and with good bone development and body growth in

The cattle grazed first the areas of barley where the drill turned around in drilling out the corners and doubled the amount of fertilizer applied. They grazed this down closely while the rest of the barley was disregarded. (Photo by E. M. Poirot, Golden City, Missouri.)

young animals. The plants' diet is out of balance for the manufacture of very much protein when that diet is growing only forests naturally. Soils in forested areas are deficient in one or more of the essential inorganic elements, and thereby deficient in furnishing a complete list of the fertility elements.

Soil Treatments Make Bigger & Better Animals

That we can apply lime, phosphate and other fertilizers and then get response by the animals has been shown: (a) by their choices in grazing of the treated soils first; (b) by their greater gains or young animal growth on forages from fertilized soils; and (c) by better reproduction on treated soils.

On many so-called "acid" soils one needs only to apply limestone, gypsum, old plaster, cement, acetylene waste or other calcium fertilizers as a streak across the pasture to see how the cattle will keep this grazed closely in contrast to the taller grass in the rest of the pasture. Such demonstrations have been numerous by the Missouri farmers, already well given to feeding their animals better by treating their soils.

Areas given phosphates and more complete fertilizers carrying nitrogen, phosphorous and potash are also similarly selected first for grazing.

Barley to be grazed was fertilized at a double rate where, by drilling out the corners, the turn was made over parts already seeded and fertilized. The doubly treated spots were taken first by the Herefords when put into the field to graze it. The cattle select not only the first crop after the soil treatment, but they keep selecting for successive crops. One Missouri farmer observed his cattle selecting one of the four haystacks each year regularly for eight years after only one single treatment was put on the surface of this virgin prairie soil. This occurred when less than five acres of the produce of the 25 in the haystack were grown on the fertilized part of the hundred acres.

Most any soil treatment that makes up a deficiency in the fertility of the soil to balance the plants' needs more completely, seems to make forage of greater preference by the grazing livestock. When the cattle exercise a choice of forage in the field, can we not expect their growth rate to be higher from it, just as we know it is for the hog exercising its choice at the self-feeder?

Experimental trials with lambs at the Missouri Agricultural Experiment Station demonstrated better gains and from the same amounts of hay consumed daily, according to the kind of fertility treatments that were put on the soils of a series of adjoining plots growing this feed. In a 63-day feeding period, soybean and lespedeza hays were grown on soils given (a) no treatment, (b) superphosphate, and (c) lime and phosphate to feed seven lambs in each pen. The animals gained eight pounds per head with the hays from the soil given no treatment. They gained 14 pounds per head during that period from the hay that was grown on soil given superphosphate. Their gain, however, mounted to 18 pounds per head when they were given the hays grown on land using the soil treatments of both lime and superphosphate.

More significant, however, than these results from the soil treatments in giving better growth were the effects on the mating with the ram the next fall. Animals were bred either with difficulty or failure in the next mating season, except those which had been fed the hays from the soil area treated with both lime and phosphate. In the purchase of hay one would scarcely ever imagine that its low quality might be cause for failure of the ewes to breed, and that it might affect returns annually on their potential reproducing power.

That building better soils also builds better herds was demonstrated forcefully by one of our Missouri Hereford breeders. Several years ago, as a beginner in growing Whitefaces on the acid soils on his farm, he decided to build up the soil as well as his herd. He has been liming, plowing down fertilizers, using legumes and, while he has been building his soil deeper, he has been highly satisfied to see that he was building the quality, health, and reproduction powers of his herd much higher. His herd is much improved over that of the nearby herd from which his was established, and which is on the originally similar soil type that has not been built up as his has.

There is plenty of evidence that on our commonly considered "acid" soils—which are in reality deficient in fertility because the fertility had to go out to let the acidity come in—we are liming them with benefit from this calcium fertilizer, not only for growing more crop bulk as tons and bushels, but also for growing our animals more efficiently and for improving their production.

Soil treatments using phosphate are proving to us that this element is put into the soil to come up through the crops, and to bring with it some synthetic effects from the plants which, like those from calcium, cannot be duplicated by putting inorganic forms of these into the mineral feed box.

Other elements are doing likewise. Copper put on the soil as only a few pounds per acre in South Australia has "cured" sheep that were producing the undesirable, so-called "steely" wool. As little as two pounds of cobalt per acre used in Scotland "cured" sheep troubles known and feared for a long time. Perhaps manganese, used as a cure for perosis in chickens when added along with these other "trace" elements as soil treatments, may soon demonstrate its value in this way also. If it, along with these others, should reduce a baffling disease like Brucellosis as may be suggested from some effects thereby on undulant fever, then better nutrition coming via the soil becomes protection against a baffling disease, and one supposedly transmitted from the animals to man. This protection would be obtained by humans according to the degree in which the animal is first protected by specific fertility additions as soil treatments.

Perhaps through relief of human misery in diseases and hidden hungers we shall find the way to banish what may be hidden hungers for our livestock, too. Out of all this may come benefits. We may eventually see that what is a healthy deficiency may go back to the deficiencies in the fertility of the soil. The time is here right now for us to build up from the soil fertility, not only the bigger profits with cattle, but also to build our own selves better in many other ways through soil conservation, just as cattlemen are building better herds by building better soils.

CHAPTER 8

Discriminations in Food Selection by Animals

THE DISCRIMINATING APPETITES of laboratory animals appear to be manifestations of the body demands for particular nutrients, as was recently demonstrated by Dr. Curt Richter. In his experiments, rats refused to eat sugar or fat when their bodies, operatively modified, could not digest these substances. When they were given increasing quantities of insulin, they ate increasing quantities of the sugar made available to them, for then their bodies could use it. They consumed large amounts of solutions of different calcium salts when their parathyroids, which control the body's use of calcium were removed.

That the appetites of farm animals are similar physiological manifestations of their nutrition needs is suggested by observations of animal choices of feeds and forages according to fertilizer treatments of the soils on which they were grown, and by the growth behaviors of animals when compelled to subsist on feeds they would of choice refuse. Farmers have reported observing some seemingly uncanny discriminating selections by animals of the same feed plant species, according to certain soil areas within a single field and between different fields.

Chemical analyses of crops giving their constituents, as carbohydrates, proteins, fats, minerals, and vitamins, are insufficient measures of their overall values for animal growth, for they have been found to depend on the finer differences in the same crop resulting from applications to the soil of limestone, phosphate, potash, or other fertilizers. When these chemicals are added to the first few inches of ground in which crops grow in amounts of only 100 or 200 pounds per acre, as is often done, they are diluted by 2,000,000 pounds of soil. Chemical methods are not sufficiently accurate to detect such small differences in the constituents of the soil, or in the crops that are grown on it, although crops are normally better even with such small additions of suitable fertilizers. But the appetites of animals as shown in selecting their feeds depending on soil treatments with fertilizers are accurate almost to inches in delineating the areas on which different fertilizers have been applied. Free choice of feed by animals, and more rapid animal growth when fed according to their choices, are now being used as refined measures of soil fertility. Heretofore the fertility of soil has been determined by its yields of farm crops per acre, but henceforth it may be done from the nutritive values of the crops produced. Some particular observations of the delicacy of animal appetites in food selections will illustrate the method.

When a new, unfenced roadway was put through a forest in the Ozark Mountains of Missouri, the question arose as to what type of tree could be used for roadside planting without danger of destruction by wild deer. The southern pine was suggested because in the adjoining forests the seedlings of this tree were not taken as browse by the deer. However, when the roadway had been planted with southern pines transplanted from the well-fertilized soils of the forest nursery, the deer that had not been taking this same species in the forest came out to the roadway and completely stripped the fertilized plantings.

Greater consumption by deer of the browse on areas in the forest receiving heavier nitrogen applications has been observed and reported in the Black Rock Forest studies. Other discriminations by wild animals as to quality of vegetation are sufficiently numerous to suggest that there is much to be learned about soil fertility by observing the appetites of wild animals and their selections of feeds according to soil differences.

Domestic animals, too, are very discriminating in their choice of foods, but offerings of herbage of single species only and the confinement of animals by fences prohibit more frequent demonstrations of these abilities. There was wisdom in the husbandman's recommendation handed down from times past that pastures should be of mixed herbage to be most efficient.

Sweet clover as pasturage is commonly refused by cattle. It is taken by them only under compulsion and after the other herbage in the fence rows and water courses has been completely consumed. Bluegrass and white clover as a mixture are a time-honored pasture herbage, but even these are taken at different rates at different periods in the grazing season, demonstrating the unerring selections by which the animal balances its diet to become sleek and fat quickly in the spring. Bluegrass growing tall and of a luscious green color in spots where there have been animal urines or droppings is also

Fig. 1. Cow chose her grass so as to have a balanced ration. Pasture grasses in mixtures, such as bluegrass and white clover, are not taken at uniform rates.

refused, as is the highly nitrogenous sweet clover. Grass in such fertilized spots continues to grow taller while the surrounding short grass is eaten shorter. Can this be due merely to the animal's fastidious taste?

As a test of this question, a part of the grass area used in a pasture project was fertilized with nitrogen alone to simulate urine addition. This much greener herbage was collected and dried along with that of an untreated plot adjoining. When these two dried harvests were used as the bulk of the diet for rabbits in feeding trials, it was found difficult to maintain them on the grass-hay from soil treated with nitrogen alone. Those on the hay from untreated soil did much better. Sweet clover, too, was fed in a similar manner and the animals "starved to it" to compel its consumption did not survive long enough to suggest other than the starvation interval. These "destructive" aspects of such feeds normally refused by the animal point to the physiological basis for the refusal. They suggest the damaging effects on animal growth of our failure to give heed to the animal's recommendation by its choices of feeds according to their beneficial physiological effects.

Most delicate discriminations by beef cattle have been observed by E. M. Poirot, of the Poirot Farms in Lawrence County, Missouri. His observations included those on animal responses to fertilizer treatments of both the cultivated soils and the virgin prairies of his extensive farm. When barley was seeded for autumn grazing and drilled with 100 pounds per acre of mixed fertilizers, the use of the tractor in wide-sweeping turns left the corners partly without seed and requiring later attention. These areas were given separate seedings that necessarily included turnings over the areas already treated and thus doubled the rate of fertilizer applications on patches of the soil near each field corner. When beef cattle were turned into these fields to graze the barley in late autumn, they selected and grazed out the areas given the double applications amounting to 200 pounds of fertilizer per acre before they took the crop on the other parts of the field. This discrimination between applications of 100 pounds and 200 pounds of fertilizer by cattle suggests that their physiological response by way of taste is more delicate and refined than most chemical tests or other measures we have been using in judging the feed values of forage.

Co-operative field trials with Mr. Poirot, in 1936, for testing the influence by soil treatments on the native flora of the virgin prairie set the stage for annual demonstrations of extraordinary animal behavior since that year. Surface applications of different fertilizers at rates not to exceed 300 pounds per acre of a single fertilizer were made in the early spring. The combinations of fertilizers were at the heaviest rate of all, but even then at only 600 pounds per acre. All treatments were drilled lightly into the soil. A goodly list of fertilizer rates was used, and a total of five acres at one end of a fenced field of 100 acres was covered with these surface applications. Observations of the changes in flora and samplings of unit areas of herbage for yield and chemical analyses were made during the summer. Later in the summer hay was made. The hay from these five treated acres was mixed with that from twenty acres without soil treatment to make one haystack. Three other haystacks were made in the field, each including the hay from twenty-five acres without soil treatment.

In late November each year more than 200 head of cattle were turned into this field to consume the four haystacks. Water and salt were provided in an adjoining pasture at the end of the row of four haystacks opposite the one containing the hay from the area given soil treatments. The cattle soon showed their keen abilities in selection by daily passing the three haystacks from the untreated area and going to consume first the stack in which the five acres of hay with soil treatments was mixed with that from the twenty untreated acres.

Fig. 2. Cattle grazing experiment. Cattle cropped the barley more closely (left) where in drilling out the field corners the fertilizer application was just about doubled.

This 100-acre area has had no soil treatments since 1936. Hay has been made and stacked in similar manner annually since that year. The cattle, too, have behaved similarly each year by demonstrating their first choice of the stack containing hay from the soil given the fertilizer treatments in 1936.

When the stack was first laid down for the eighth demonstration in 1943, it was too small to take the hay from the five acres treated in 1936, and all of the hay in addition from the twenty acres untreated as customarily put into this stack with it. Consequently, a part of the hay from this untreated area was built-on as an extension of the stack. The cattle cut this stack in two at the juncture of these two stackings by consuming first that part which included the five acres formerly treated, and by leaving unconsumed the end made up wholly of untreated hay. They then distributed themselves amongst all the stacks in the field, including this remnant that had no greater lure for them than the untreated hay in the other three stacks.

In October 1944 when the cattle were turned into the field with the stacks, no frost having come to kill the grass before mid-November, the cattle took to the grass and not to the hay. They grazed persistently on the limited acreage where the soil had once been fertilized. When they finally took to the hay, they failed to select so pronouncedly the stack with a small part of its bulk made up of hay from fertilized land. Evidently the effects of the fertilizer were still recognizable in the grass, but not in the hay when this was diluted in the haystack with unfertilized hay by a ratio of one to five. Unfortunately, there was no stack made solely of fertilized hay to test this question more accurately.

The delicacy of the appetite of the cattle is clearly demonstrated by giving consideration to the following factors in the case. No more than 600 pounds of fertilizer was put on the surface of the soil. It was subjected to an average annual rainfall of 35 inches during eight years. Nine crops of hay have been removed. The treated hay each year was diluted so as to make up only one part in five of the preferred stack. And in the eighth year the animals were still passing by the three stacks from unfertilized land and selecting the fourth. By the ninth year they were still recognizing the fertilizer effects in the grass, but not in the hay mixed with so much from soils without treatment. Surely, in the light of this evidence the animals' choice must be recognized as a refinement in detecting differences in the crop coming by way of the soil that chemistry as yet cannot duplicate.

Hogs, as grain eaters, point out by their selection of food that soil treatments register in the differences in the grain, as was demonstrated in forages by the cattle choices. Mr. Virgil Burk, formerly the county agent of Johnson County, Missouri, reported the remarkable discrimination of hogs in "hogging down" corn on the farm of Mr. Cliff Long. These animals, when turned into a large field, went to its opposite end to take grain first where the soil had previously been limed; and they passed daily through the untreated corn in going to and from the water and protein supplement.

The hog has long been credited with discriminating ability as a balancer of its diet. It was Professor Evvard, of Iowa State College, the creator of the self-feeder idea and observer of the hog as a balancer of its diet, who said, "The pig, if given a chance, will make a hog of itself in less time than you will." This uncanny capacity of the hog to exercise choice was used to demonstrate differences in the quality of corn grown on plots with different soil treatments on Sanborn Field, Columbia, Missouri. Since a number of these adjoining plots, in their crop rotations, were to have corn, it was planted across them, several corn hybrids being chosen for the experiment. This arrangement made it possible to sample the corn according to each hybrid and also for the hogs to select according to each plot with a different soil fertility treatment.

Each hybrid was harvested by its particular hills on each plot. A sample was put into a bag, labeled by plot and by hybrid and put away for storage. The remainder of the corn was saved separately by plot without hybrid segregation. This balance of the corn was put into self-feeders with the particular hybrid mixture from each plot in a separate compartment, in 100 pound units, to permit easy report of percentage consumption. When the supply in any compartment was low, the corn remaining in each one was weighed, and the arrangement with respect to compartments and plots was changed as each was again filled with corn from a plot with a particular soil treatment. Sufficient grain was available to carry out this weighing and rearranging several times.

It was significantly interesting that, regardless of the distribution of the corn among the different compartments in the self-feeder, there was each time the same order of consumption of the grain relative to the soil treatments. Since the corn consisted of mixtures of hybrid breedings in each feeder compartment, a segregated selection by the hogs according to the various hybrids was impossible. The weights of the animals were not kept, nor was any measure attempted of the greater efficiency in making pork through animal selection. But this greater efficiency was reported for rats by Dr. Curt Richter who demonstrated that when permitted choice of the separate ingredients of a common feed mixture, they made the same gains on less feed than when compelled to take the mixture.

As confirmatory of the choice of food by hogs, observations were made of native rats which were not given open access to whole grains because the corn was stored in bags. Samples in small bags of different hybrids and from different plots—though considered carefully stored—were attacked by rats. The bags happened to be piled so that every one was accessible, and the choice of the rats was demonstrated by bags which were found to be cut and those which were left unharmed. Surprising as it may seem, the choice of bags cut by the rats agreed closely by plots and soil treatments with the choices by the hogs. The rats did not distinguish between the hybrids on the same plots within the limited number of choices available in this demonstration. This suggests that the soil on which grain grows, rather than the pedigree of its breeding, is the basic factor that is reflected in the delicacy of the appetite in food selection by animals.

Just what particular chemical compound in the food helps the animal to discriminate and whether it does so by smell, as well as by taste, are still open questions. Very delicate differences are even recognized by chicks, as was demonstrated by Dr. Weston A. Price in testing their ability to dis-

Fig. 3. Hogs chose the best corn. Choice by hogs of corn grown on treated soil exactly marked out this area as they daily ate it before taking corn grown on untreated soil.

criminate the differences in contents of Vitamin A and "activator X" in butter. Even for butter as an animal physiological product—seemingly far removed from the soil—of which three grades varying in contents of these two catalytic agents were weighed out daily, put into different positions in the brooder, and weighed back regularly, the chicks selected and ate about two and one-half times as much of the butter high in the "activator X" as of that which was low. The selection was in accordance with the better survival and growth as brought on by these differences in the butter in other tests. This selection by the chicks occurred when neither Dr. Price nor any member of his staff could distinguish between the butters.

The ancient art of agriculture has handed down practices often frowned upon by its youthful science. But when it is now reported that vitamins are generated through microbial activities in the cow's paunch, we may appreciate the soundness of the old practice of hogs following fattening steers to gather the undigested corn. Interdependence of animals, as demonstrated in the importance of providing animal products in the diets for carnivorously inclined pigs and chickens, while cows and sheep are truly herbivorous,

NO TREATMENT   SOIL TREATMENT

Fig. 4. Effect of diet on rabbits left. Rabbit fed hay from unfertilized soil. Right, rabbit fed hay from treated soil. Note differences in size of bones and appearance.

suggests the possible use of the animal appetite as a new tool for the assay of feeds, and for the measure of the levels of soil fertility producing them.

That the animal's delicacy in selecting food serves for its better body growth is clearly suggested in work to date. That the soil's contribution of fertility in more generous and in better-balanced amounts is provocative of these choices has not been widely considered. Animal assays of soil fertility to much more refined degrees than are possible by chemical tests are now being used to learn just what treatments a soil needs in order to make its herbage products an efficient forage or hay. In the final analysis, pasture studies must submit to this criterion which the animal itself imposes.

Better body growth is not the only measure by which the products from treated soils are shown to be superior. Better reproduction is another criterion to which soil treatments must cater by way of the feeds as modified by them. The use of rabbits for artificial insemination permitted feeding to one group lespedeza hay grown on soil given phosphate, and to another group the same kind of plant grown on adjoining plots where both lime and phosphate were the soil treatments. After only three weeks the males feeding on the first of these hays had become indifferent to a female in oestrus and were unable to deliver viable semen in regular amounts. Those on the second hay remained readily excitable on the appearance of the female in oestrus and continued efficient in their semen delivery. After the interchange of the hays for the two groups of males, three weeks was a long enough period to reverse their reactions. It is a significant suggestion that the animal's selection of its feeds reaches not only into body functions measured by increase in body mass, but also into those which serve to maintain the species.

More studies will be required before we can use the animal appetites, animal growth, and animal reproduction as refined techniques for the most complete assay of soil fertility. To date, however, animal behaviors have given some very encouraging results to suggest that the student of soils has in the animal itself a detecting instrument, the delicacy of which approaches that of the chemist's spectrograph. When the physiology behind the appetite is more generally understood and when organic differences in the body are connected with, or provocative of distinct manifestations of the appetite, we shall be in better position to handle our soils for more efficient health and growth of the animals. What this promising approach can do for human health is still an unexplored field. Increasing food problems on a national scale suggest that we should call in all aids to make our soils more efficient as food producers. The delicacy of animal appetite in food selections is one such help that warrants early and wider acceptance.

CHAPTER 9

The Influence of Soil Mineral Elements on Animal Nutrition

A CENTENNIAL ANNIVERSARY is naturally a significant occasion in the history of an institution in the United States. With the turn of the hundredth year one is reminded that such length of time in prospect seems tremendous. But a corresponding time in retrospect seems short. The prophetic view is never so clear in its portent as is the postmortem. Hindsight has always been much more instructive than foresight. The former makes mental impressions with accompanying stronger and more disturbing emotions, hence is more of a modifier and determiner of our future behavior than is the latter.

But in an agricultural experiment station, where the living, i.e. the biological, more than the dead, or the technological, matters concern us, we have numerous and significant postmortems regularly. This seems more true now with so much emphasis on economics and sociology, when the cleaning away of disasters and the covering of defects of past mistakes occupy our thought almost to the exclusion of the preventive viewpoint. We scarcely have time to look ahead and to each visions. We miss the chance to theorize as to how man can fit himself on to his agriculture, required to feed all of us, and into the laws of Nature, including both those recorded and those not yet comprehended.

But anniversaries are occasions encouraging us to look ahead, and to profit by means of what is behind the anniversary date. The extrapolation and the reach into the future, however theoretical and short of proof that stretch of vision is, may well "let us study things as they are and not as we have made them. Let us question our beliefs to see whether they really fit the facts. If they don't let's cast them out." Anniversaries are times permitting decided shifts in viewpoints which may be a healthful experience occasionally even for some sections of an Agricultural Experiment Station and a College of Agriculture.

The Subject

The subject "The Influence of Soil Mineral Elements on Animal Nutrition" as assigned for discussion on this occasion, reminds us that the production of animals and their service to man for his food, clothing and even shelter, is an art older than man's recorded history. The importance of an adequate supply of forage for the well-being of the herds and the flocks, and thereby for man, has long been well recognized. The ancient writings in The Great Book of all books point out the need for grass. They discuss the capacity of the land to grow crops in sufficient support of the cattle lest there be strife between the herdsmen and between the herd owners. There are suggestions from ancient authors to indicate that, even before the Roman era, men were aware that plants are no better than the soils on which they grow, and animals are no healthier than the plants which nourish them. Not quite so long ago, Izaak Walton, in his *The Compleat Angler* pointed out that the soil fertility is a factor in determining the quality of sheep wool, and in the tastiness of the trout. "And so I shall proceed next to tell you" he says, "it is certain that certain fields near Leominster, a town in Herefordshire, are observed to make sheep that graze upon them more fat than the next, and also to bear finer wool; that is to say, that in that year in which they feed in a particular pasture, they shall yield finer wool than they did that year before they came to feed upon it, and coarser again if they shall return to their former pasture; and again return to a finer wool, being fed on the finer wool ground. Which I tell you that you may better believe that I am certain, if I catch a trout in one meadow he shall be white and faint, and very likely to be lousy; and as certainly as if I catch a trout in the next meadow, he shall be strong and red and lusty and much better meat; trust me, scholar, I have caught many a trout in a particular meadow, that the very shape and enameled color of him was made such as hath joyed me to look on him; and I have then with much pleasure concluded with Solomon, 'Everything is beautiful in its season'."

Izaak Walton in that observation of 300 years ago saw the difference in the health, in the wool, in the quality of the fiber, in the sheen of the body color, in the quality of the muscle meat, and even in the presence or the absence of insect infestations of the beast and the fish in the fields and the streams, all related to the fertility of the soil. Our subject for discussion is then an old and a long familiar theme to the keen observing naturalist even though to us as scientists it may seem still new, strange, and not entirely proved.

The Ecological, or Deductive Approach

In dealing with this subject, "The Influence of Soil Mineral Elements on Animal Nutrition," one might consider two methods of approach, either (a) the inductive one which would study each inorganic element and tabulate its nutritional services to the plant and to the animal under experiment and then from that collection of data would piece together and tell the final story; or (b) the deductive one, which may be considered the ecological approach. In the latter, by studying Nature's pattern of animal placement in different areas, i.e. according to the ecological pattern, we would learn the soil differences as to mineral elements representing causes of animal presence and animal absence according to the natural processes of evolution. This is a qualitative attack and not a quantitative one. It notes the presence or absence of certain products and not how much or how well. In this discussion we shall use mainly the ecological or the deductive approach as a good beginning. We shall observe and investigate Nature's pattern and by both deduction and experimental inductions find reasons for Her locating animals on some soils and not on others. Then we might possibly deduce, there-from, the roles of the different minerals, or the soil fertility elements in plant nutrition and thereby in animal nutrition, at least by the way they cause animal absence or the animal's failure to survive.

In this approach we shall accept the American bison's presence in great herds upon the Plains as evidence of a fairly good array of mineral elements in the soil there, or, at least, of very good combined influence on animal nutrition through the virgin forages grown there. It avoids the distorted view of nutrition which too often is mainly a fattening process, and then one of a castrated male with a very limited life span, demonstrating all too little of nutrition for the procreation and survival of the species.

By using this soil pattern with the areas of soil minerals of high and favorable influence on the survival of the bison as the guide and starting point, we are impressed with the large land areas of virgin soils of mineral or fertility contents too deficient in only one or two nutrient elements for the survival of this quadraped. We should also be impressed by the applicability of those ecological facts to our cattle herds and other livestock when the bison on those soils was duplicating our domestic animals in many details of their physiological complexities: (a) of growth, (b) of body protection against disease, and (c) of reproduction of high fecundity for survival of the species without the help (or interference) of man and his agriculture.

The Anatomy of the Ruminant
Connects it More Closely with the Soil

Since the bison is a ruminant and the herds of the Plains lived by forages, or roughages, in considerable bulk and not by masses of grains and other concentrates, our view of the animals in this discussion may well be limited to the ruminants also. With the paunch as a digestive or fermenting vat at the head-end rather than the tail-end of the cow's alimentary canal, the forage she ingests brings with it the soil microflora and microfauna for action in the anaerobic conditions there. By that fact she lets us connect her more closely with the soil. She profits by those symbiotic microbial relations, especially when her ingestion of urea within limits and its service as protein supplement bears the suggestion that its chemical structure with the amino nitrogen attached to the carbon serves so much more efficiently than does ammonia nitrogen or other nitrogen forms not so closely similar to the amino acid structure of protein as is urea. That she has some advantage for survival on forages only by that particular anatomical arrangement and microbial symbiosis of the paunch is suggested by the close companionship in which the pig and the chicken have always held her as one of the barnyard family by following on the heels of the cow so closely to feed on her droppings of dung but not of the urine. When the pig and the chicken have their microbial digestive helps within the alimentary canal at the tail-end of it, they are not so closely connected with, nor so completely supported by, the soil as the cow is. That the flora and fauna of the cow's paunch respond to the differences in "ash" minerals coming in the forage as feed from the soils of differing fertility was illustrated by the higher amounts of volatile fatty acids resulting from the same ration in the rumen (artificial) according as there was added the ash of alfalfa grown on the more fertile soil types or the soil more carefully fertilized.

We may well consider the bison as the early ruminant fauna outlining a pattern of animal survival according to fertility pattern exhibited by the mineral or inorganic elements in the soil. Then by considering the cow as a physiological duplicate to be scattered for her survival over the same geographic area, the problem does not necessarily require our being certain that we can prescribe the array of soil fertility elements complete enough in list and functions to give certain specific results for economic management of the herds of cattle. It would be also a vain presumption to believe that we have obtained that much organized knowledge about the soil and its capacity for creating livestock. Rather by studying the soils and their natural flora in the areas where, and by which, the bison survived in contrast to the fringes and areas outside of his concentration where he was extinguished, we can detect more nearly one or two inorganic elements of which the shortage may be limiting the forage production in amount and in quality for the survival of our agricultural ruminant, the cow. Even then the problem soon becomes one of combinations and permutations, rather than single element research, in a long list when several fertility elements may be missing and many more of them may be in imbalance for the growth of the forages of sufficient quality for even ruminant species survival under the handicap of our domestication.

The Interpretation of the Soil as Complete Animal Nutrition Challenges Wisdom of Both Cow and Man

In considering the soil mineral elements in animal nutrition by way of the ecological pattern of the area like the United States, the size of the problem is already disheartening when, (a) by the soil as a contributor to animal feeding in a concentrated way like agriculture, less than 10 percent of the earth's crust serves for farming; and (b) by the plants, only about 5 percent of the sun's energy is used; and (c) by the animals, less than 25 percent of their feed is converted by the livestock into food for our use. This would indicate that all the weathering, all the geological, all the volcanic, or other changes on the earth's surface have not been philanthropically getting the chemical array of soil minerals collected into the soil with nutrition of domestic or even wild animals in prospect everywhere.

In considering the subject of the close nutritional connection between soil fertility and animal nutrition then, should we be appalled when the soil hinders the survival of so many domestic animals because of their multiplying numbers of diseases, their increasing degeneration, and their failing reproduction? Should we not recognize our lack of knowledge of how the animals feed themselves in Nature or how we survived when the cow as a perambulating soil chemist and soil tester went ahead of the plow to lead us to fertile soils on our westward march? Recognizing that scant collection of facts, not even organized into a science on that subject, we would seemingly have ample reason in humility to congratulate the cow on her survival in spite of us when we changed the order and have now put the plow ahead of the cow while we are acting as the chemists and the soil testers presuming to serve in the creation of her species. That we have learned about some few of the soil minerals to be applied separately, as fertilizers, for better animal nutrition by way of the forage crops we grow, indicates the magnitude of the problem. That we have not yet juggled all the nutrient elements of the soil into the proper combination; that we have not yet found the collection of crop plants to be grown on that suite of them in the field, should not be at all surprising. If then we have not arrived at the level of knowledge giving complete diagnosis of the cow's deficient health and failing reproduction, or if we have not yet written the complete prescription in commercial fertilizers from the chemist's shop by which the problems of animal nutrition will shift into regular and satisfactory profit, we should not be appalled. The many processes of creation which originate in the handful of dust have not had much more elucidation in terms of physiological chemistry even today than was implied in that allegorically reported way of merely starting them from the soil as given us in the record of a few thousand years ago. The past century has opened our minds to the soil fertility as potential plant and animal nutrition, but the *modus operandi* of each of the essential or non-essential elements in that service is a challenge remaining to be met in the next hundred years and reported at the next centennial celebration.

Essential Elements Represent Widely Different Groups & Properties in their Classification

At the outset it may be well to list the so-called "essential" elements for plant growth included up to this moment in our growing knowledge of them periodically well summarized. It might be well to characterize them by groupings according to certain chemical properties, reactions, or services in the physiology of the microbes, plants and animals. Among those composing most of the plant bulk, thereby the most combustible plant parts, are carbon, hydrogen and oxygen. These make up the carbohydrates into which by reductive changes three others are combined, namely nitrogen, sulfur and phosphorus. These changes of the carbohydrates, which are serving as starter compounds in the plant's synthetic performances, make the proteins and other compounds closely associated with them like the enzymes, the hormones, etc. Of these six elements just listed, four, namely the carbon, hydrogen, oxygen and nitrogen are commonly considered as coming, not from the soil, but from the atmosphere and water in the ultimate. But while the plant nitrogen of ultimate atmospheric origin, is taken by most of them from the soils via organic matter transformed there, so we are realizing slowly that carbon, hydrogen, and oxygen, also of ultimate atmospheric origin, may be going more directly into the plant as organic compounds taken from the soil. The soil is the medium through which the fertility contributions from the atmosphere make their way. These six elements are spoken of as constituents of the "structural organic" part of the crops.

Among the elements more commonly connected with the ash, or noncombustible part of the plant, are the alkalies and the alkaline earths, i.e. potassium and sodium in the former and calcium and magnesium in the latter group. Among the elements required in trace amounts for plants are the heavy metals, manganese, iron, zinc, copper and molybdenum; and the light metal boron, to which may eventually be added the light metal silicon if we ever consider it essential for plants as its general presence in them might lead us to believe, though plants grow without it. Very recently chlorine has been demonstrated as required for plant growth. Other elements may be considered essential for the plant when it serves to deliver them within itself as essentials for the animal. In the case of silicon, not considered essential, much of it is found in hoof and hair of the animals. But, since it is one of the chemically sluggish performers, we have not yet decided that it is essential for animal growth even though present in larger measure in plants as, in general, they serve less effectively in animal nutrition. In the above list of seventeen elements essential for plant growth there need to be emphasized the two, namely sodium and chlorine as required for the animals in quantity and then to be added are the iodine, the cobalt, and possibly the fluorine required in trace amounts for animals but not so recognized for plants.

In addition to considering those elements coming from the soil for benefit, one dares not omit the soil-borne elements of which extra supplies there may be entering the plant for harmful effects. Among those considered non-essential but injurious to both plants and animals are arsenic and selenium. Among those both essential in trace amounts and possibly injurious in large amounts are boron, manganese, copper and fluorine.

Among the seventeen elements so far considered essential for plant growth and the three or more required for animals, the ultimate origins of four, that is, carbon, hydrogen, nitrogen, oxygen, in the atmosphere and the hydrosphere may be reason for omitting these four in discussing the soil mineral elements in animal nutrition. If so, we must concern ourselves with only thirteen elements coming from the soil by way of the plants, whether their separate services are known or unknown there, and going into the animal by way of the feed taken. They are going into the animals as combinations within the organic matter composing the forages consumed and not as minerals or salts. For purpose of this discussion let us consider the animal's taking to salts as a case of ministration of relief on our part or a kind of depravity of the animal's appetite equivalent to the chewing of bones occasionally exhibited by some of the starving cattle as an act of desperation.

Elements' Activities for Retention in the Soil & Entrance into the Plant Root are Foremost Criteria

As another classification of the mineral elements in animal nutrition, one might list their anatomical location, or their presence in larger amounts of each in different body parts. But more helpful than these "ash analyses" by areas of anatomy, are the location of the elements by physiology or function in the plant first and then in the animal. But rather than undertaking these considerations it would be helpful to note the geo-chemo-dynamics by which the elements are held in the soil and are active there in entering the plant root. Thus we would work in the element's course "from the ground up" to the animal, and not in reverse from the animal back to the soil.

Our knowledge of plant nutrition in terms of the soil-borne elements, in the form of clearer concepts of how these are held in the soil and how their activities move them from there into the plant root, has built itself up for only some of the positively charged ions. Calcium, magnesium, potassium, ammonium, nitrogen, and sodium are in this cation group now that the commonly larger quantities of them have allowed us to connect them with a negatively charged colloidal clay molecule and to study their activities there. As for the trace elements with the positive charge, naturally, they can also be held by the clay except for the chlorine as an anion.

But their active movement from that site and their nutritional services to the plant have not been demonstrated as is true for the above few. Their trace or limited quantities have kept them outside of the pale of our comprehension and precise tabulation.

Our concepts of how the anions or negatively charged ions of nutritive service to the plants are held in the soil and mobilized into the plant root have not taken on geo-chemical, or physico-chemical, or biochemical stature equivalent of that we now conceive for the major cations. This inorganic half of the nutrient elements, namely the anions, is still in that mental haze regarding basic chemical behaviors which we exhibit when we speak so commonly of "available" or "extractable" nutrients. When the anions are adsorbed on positively charged colloidal plastics, their exchange activities from there into the plant root simulate those of the cations held by and exchanged from the clay colloid. We have been content up to this moment with concepts only of cationic exchange when we know that no cation exists without a corresponding cation. We seem oblivious to the fact that for ions in nature there is no contented state of bachelorship.

Likewise our concepts of what organic compounds may be taken directly from the soil are not well developed though for the inorganic anions like nitrate and sulfate we look to decaying organic matter of the soil. For the anion phosphate, we know little more than its "fixed" or "extractable" states, yet it is highly essential in the transformation of carbohydrates both in photosynthesis and in respiration. The most neglected anion may perhaps be the bicarbonate with its origin in respiration, when this is so universally present in the rhizosphere and when plant nutrition is so readily disturbed by very small amounts of fertilizer anions (chlorides and sulfates) applied on soils of lower contents of decaying organic matter. The neglect of the anions in our thinking seems to be as serious as is the neglect of the carbon compounds or the organic substances taken by the plant root as compounds directly from the soil. This latter, however, is a growing phase of our knowledge and may be all the more significant if it is connected, as some observations suggest, with protein synthesis by the plant, especially with possibly the amino acids tryptophane and methionine, so commonly deficient in forages and feeds.

The Limiting Element
is Limiting More Than Itself

The single element as a lone variable is the standard scientific procedure in research. However, in biological behaviors, like plant nutrition, the single varied element for plant root entrance does not vary in plant entrance itself without inducing variation in the entrance there of many others and consequent variations in the amounts of them in the final growth products. In the cationic suite on the colloidal clay these interrelations and intereffects of the cations are demonstrated by the fact that while calcium occurs in amounts up to 60 or 85 percent of the soil's cation exchange capacity, magnesium makes up 6 to 8 percent, and potassium but 2 to 5 percent for good plant growth, yet the plant contains more potassium than of either of the other two. Also, a small variation in the potassium supply when both of the other two are constant, gives variations in the amounts of these divalents, calcium and magnesium, entering into the plant. This holds true not only under experimental control but is also demonstrated in the ecological array of plants according to the increasing degree of development of the soil under the climatic forces of rainfall and temperature.

Other interrelations and intereffects not only between two, but between multiple cations suggest themselves as a regular order according to increasing numbers of studies of plant nutrition using the colloidal clay and the amberlite absorption techniques for control of cations and anions, respectively, for test of the resulting variations in the plant's composition in either the inorganic or organic aspects. A growing knowledge of the significance of these ratios of exchangeable cations and their activities measured by means of soil tests and specially constructed membrane electrodes respectively for the nutrition of different plants, and their respective chemical compositions, is rendering much help in managing the fertility of the soil as a balanced diet for plants with emphasis on their photosynthesis of carbohydrates mainly or on also their biosynthesis of more proteins. We are gradually modifying the plant's composition by different balances in fertility for different final plant make-up much as we balance the animal ration differently when we grow an animal than when we fatten it.

In some recent studies, the variation of the exchangeable amounts in the soil of any one of five of the inorganic nutrient elements offered brome grass induced variation not only in the entrance into the plant of the other four nutrient elements from the soil, but also gave varied synthesis by the plant of each of the sixteen measured organic compounds. These latter included four carbohydrates and twelve amino acids. With reference to the carbohydrate synthesis by these experimental plants, the soil-borne element, potassium, influenced the accumulation of metabolizable sugars. When potassium was high, the sugars and starch in the plants were high. But when the soil nitrogen was high, the metabolizable sugars were present in still much higher concentrations. An interdependence of these two soil-borne elements, namely, potassium and nitrogen, was thus clearly demonstrated for carbohydrate synthesis. When phosphorus, however, was the variable and both nitrogen and potassium were constant, there occurred wide variations in the concentrations of the several carbohydrate fractions, that is, the reducing sugars, the non-reducing sugars, the starch and the hemi-cellulose. That calcium played a part in the cycle of carbohydrate synthesis, a belief not held by many, was clearly established by the fact that carbohydrates as metabolizable sugars were higher in concentration in the brome grass when calcium and the other soil-borne elements were high than when calcium was low with the others all higher. These four elements, potassium, nitrogen, phosphorus, and calcium, each as a single variable modified the array in the plant of the four fractions of the carbohydrates.

In the amino acids synthesis, calcium played a fundamental role. Plants grown on high calcium and high-nitrogen soils were higher in the individual amino acids than those grown on soil low in calcium, but adequately supplied with the nitrogen. High concentrations of several of the amino acids found in the brome grass were the resultants of high calcium, moderate potassium, and high anion fertilization, namely with phosphorous, sulfur, and nitrogen. More amino acids were produced in less bulk of the brome grass than on other treatments of much higher yields of bulk. Wide differences in the relative distribution of amino acids were shown to depend very decidedly on the soil treatment.

In this study the amounts of total nitrogen as percentage of dry weight were sorely discredited as a criterion of protein quality as amino acids in the crops. Several of the amino acids essential for animal nutrition, namely isoleucine, threonine, methionine and tryptophane were quite low with high-nitrogen and high-calcium treatments of the soil, yet the total nitrogen of the plants was high. In these cases most of the nitrogen was present in aspartic acid, arginine and lysine. It was shown that the application of nitrogen to the soil and the high nitrogen concentrations of the plant would not guarantee the presence of a good array of the amino acids essential for good animal nutrition.

Several amino acids were present in almost the same relative amounts in each treatment, and though variable in concentrations with soil treatments, they were present in more or less constant ratios. This held true for methionine and tryptophane in relation to some of the others. Isoleucine and threonine suggested a similar behavior. This fact suggested that these amino acids, particularly methionine, which was invariably in low concentrations, could be used as an index of protein quality with more reliability than could the concentration of the total nitrogen.

Thus, while we are apt to believe that we are setting a single element as a limiting or controlled one in the fertility of the soil as a simple, scientific experimental procedure, we cannot speak with truth of it as if a single variable were the cause of the varied plant's composition when the variations of the other fertility elements entering the plants from the soil are contemporaneously so extensive and so numerous. Thus we are in no position to single out any inorganic fertility element in the soil and believe that its variation there can be measured as a specific influence on animal nutrition so directly as ash delivery of it in the forage fed. Not even nitrogen analyses, multiplied by a factor and called crude protein, can bear much significance. The influence of any single element on animal nutrition must be viewed in terms of its service within the plant through which the synthetic performances by the forage crop render this vegetative mass more nearly a balanced diet for (a) the growing of animals, (b) the making of them more healthy, and (c) the encouragement of their more fecund reproduction. It is in these helps toward the survival of the species more than helps in serving our whims or particular desires for a certain effect, like fattening only, that we need to learn more about soil fertility as plant nutrition in order that this soil property may be more helpful in animal nutrition.

The Trace Elements & the Essential Amino Acids Under Bioassay

When the different carbohydrates, including reducing sugars, non-reducing sugars, starch, and hemi-cellulose are not each a specific requirement in supplying energy for the ruminant but serve quite interchangeably, and when the proteins are very probably a matter of a set of specific amounts and kinds of amino acids, it would seem quite clear that the production of more complete proteins in terms of those essential amino acids should be the measure of the influences by the soil-mineral elements on animal nutrition. When there has always been such serious need in humid regions for protein supplements even in the feeding for fattening purposes this need suggests that we should visualize, not a shortage of crude proteins or nitrogenous compounds, but such of the limiting amino acids in animal nutrition connected with some limiting inorganic elements in the soil as the cause of the trouble.

With this view as the theory, it seemed well to test the shifted ratios of calcium to other elements, for example, as these modify plant compositions, since it has been the common concept that calcium-deficient (acid) soils do not grow the more proteinaceous or leguminous crops as the better feeds. By varying the amounts of the exchangeable calcium only, or of other ions in ratio to calcium, many changes were brought about in the crop's composition, as both inorganic and organic criteria can measure them, to say nothing of the wide, readily visible differences in the mass and appearances of the crop. It has been extensively demonstrated that the photosynthetic performances of piling up carbohydrate bulk as forages are influenced by variations in the supplies and ratios of the inorganic fertility elements. The high yields of low-protein corn running well over the hundred-bushel-per-acre mark and the increasing yields of low protein or "soft wheat" are ample evidence. But the concentration even of crude protein in that bulk is disturbed decidedly by the soil's inorganic fertility, while more disturbed is the protein which results in seed production. Still more modified by the inorganic and organic fertility of the soil is the specific array of amino acids within especially the forage but also in the seed. We need to judge the influence of the inorganic fertility according as it prompts the synthesis by the plants of a balanced suite of required amino acids in the feed crops we grow.

When we burn the vegetation in sulfuric acid in our chemical determination of crude protein and assume that all of the nitrogen is protein nitrogen, we forget that some of the nitrogen may serve in metabolism of the animal, as is true for the amino nitrogen of tryptophane, while an equal part of nitrogen in that amino acid is eliminated in unchanged chemical structure as is the indole ring nitrogen of that essential part of complete protein. In this case of the measure of the crude protein represented for tryptophane, then, we make an error of 100 percent as regards metabolizable nitrogen. For this reason it has been deemed a more refined measure of the influence of the soil fertility on animal nourishment by way of the vegetation grown, to study the shift in amino acid array in forages as influenced by the inorganic soil fertility.

Of particular interest have been the trace elements as they influence the amino acids, tryptophane and methionine. Of course, the sulfur of the soil in relation to the latter, has been challenging since methionine is the significant sulfur-containing amino acid. Tryptophane synthesis by alfalfa and soybeans was decreased when magnesium, boron, manganese and iron were withheld. The effects were shown to be similar whether in nutrient solution or in colloidal clay cultures.

The synthesis of methionine by these same legumes, alfalfa and soybeans, showed regular increase with the increased addition of sulfur to give the characteristic sigmoid curve. Here again these effects were exhibited by both the solution and the soil cultures. Sudan grass increased its methionine content also when flowers of sulfur were the fertilizer treatment of the soil. The increase of this particular amino acid occurred when there was not necessarily a significant increase in the total nitrogen. All of this indicates that we cannot expect the array of the amino acids to be contingent on a certain percent of total nitrogen. These two commonly deficient amino acids, tryptophane and methionine, may be increased in relation to some of the other amino acids, while in relation to others they seem to maintain a nearly constant ratio.

Timothy hay in its assay by rabbits demonstrated nicely that the fertilization with trace elements in addition to the major elements, according to soil tests, gave wide variation in the efficiency of the hay, supplemented by wheat, for adding weight to growing weanlings. But even with the trace elements, the wheat-timothy hay combination allowed the heat wave of 1954 to kill off the rabbits, when the stock rabbits on the same wheat supplemented by green grass suffered no losses by such death.

Relative to the possible protein in question, the addition of dried skim milk powder to the wheat-timothy hay was also an antidote for the dangerous heat wave, as was the green grass. As a repeat of the experiment under the extended heat wave, red clover hay was substituted for the timothy hay after the fatalities on the latter had mounted to 30 percent in contrast to 70 percent in the first experiment. There were no fatalities by the accommodating heat wave after the red clover was substituted. Accordingly, red clover hay and dried skim milk powder appeared as equals in preventing deaths from the heat wave by rabbits fed on wheat and timothy hay fertilized by full treatments including the separate trace elements, manganese, boron, copper, zinc, molbydenum, and then by all of these in combination.

There is the suggestion that the timothy hay, one of the grasses, under full fertilization including even trace elements is not equal to the red clover for synthesizing some of the compounds required by the nutrition of the rabbit if it is to survive the higher temperatures of the summer. But there is also the suggestion that red clover, one of the once-favored forage feeds but now about extinct on the farms, can synthesize some organic help for the survival of the rabbit on dry feed during a severe summer heat wave.

Relative to the vitamins in the green grass in contrast to the dry timothy and red clover hays, no assays were made for their content of these essentials. In some previous studies of ascorbic acid in spinach, according to the decreasing amounts of calcium and nitrogen offered as soil fertility, there was the suggestion of increased concentration of ascorbic acid with partial decrease in fertility, and then a decided decrease of this vitamin with further lowering of the fertility. There was thus a striking correlation of vitamin C with the mineral composition of the plant as dependent on the fertility of the soil in that respect.

Whether the rabbit discriminates in feed choice according to the vitamin C concentration was not tested. But that rabbits feeding on cracked corn grain will select the germ in preference to the endosperm to increase the protein in their feed consumption was well demonstrated. By limiting the hay as a supplement to cracked corn and supplying a fresh grain allotment after 25, 50, and 75 percent of the total had been consumed, the rabbits discrimination had increased the protein in the part consumed by 12, 6, and 3 percent, respectively, according to weights and analyses of the remnant grain samples. Accordingly, as the higher discrimination was exercised, the gain in weight per unit of feed was less. This suggests that the rabbit does not choose to be fattened by the starch of the corn if there is protein to be selected in preference.

Summary

According to the preceding details reported in studies aimed to interpret the soil fertility as nutrition for the plants and the animals consuming the plants, we have not seen so much influence by the soil on animal nutrition when merely increased vegetative bulk as larger yields by the crop and increased animal weight by fattening have been the criteria aiming to interpret the influence of the mineral fertility content of the soil as it modifies the animal nutrition. Ash analyses of the crop, or of the animal, have not served as significant indicators of the influences by the soil fertility on agricultural products or their values as feed and food. They have demonstrated such in rumenology. Crude protein as an ash analysis of nitrogen multiplied by an arbitrary factor has also been disappointing. But when the protein as a suite of essential amino acids in the plants is considered, then the fertility of the soil suggests that it has influence on what organic compounds the plant synthesizes, especially the array of amino acids required as complete protein. Different crops differ in their potentiality of synthesizing these in array suggesting better animal nutrition in some crops than in others through these more complete arrays of amino acids.

Nature has given its different life forms a decidedly high safety factor. For example, we have two lungs and two kidneys, yet we find no manifestation in the malfunction of the first until there is malfunction of the second. As the result of this safety factor, subclinical troubles in animals must be numerous but go unrecognized. So in this problem of providing the soil minerals in proper balance for animal and human nutrition, two aspects deserve special mention; "There is danger in assuming that no degree of deficiency exists in the absence of common incidence of observable, recognizable symptoms usually associated with gross deficiency;" and "The effects of mineral deficiency are not confined to those conditions directly due to the deficiency." We now recognize hidden hungers and the side or secondary reactions in organic chemistry as well as the primary one. So the soil as the starting point in agricultural production may also start many side reactions along its assembly line, working up from the soil through the microbe and the plant to the animal's nutrition. Consequently, deficiencies of subclinical magnitude have been multiplying with the decline of soil fertility, to where the incidence of the microbe is a biological suggestion of incipient body degeneration started by hidden hungers. For too long a time we have fought the microbe as if it were the entire "disease." Soil deficiencies may well be setting up the invitations for the microbes and all that we are prone to label "disease."

We are slowly coming to see that the increasing deficiencies in the soil under its cultivation have shifted the crops we grow to those of less protein and less inorganic contents. They are thereby giving less complete nutrition for the animal's self-preservation when higher fertility of the soil has been demonstrating itself as protection for the plants against fungi and insects. The larger ecological pattern has exhibited the soil as a factor via the mineral fertility elements in locating the wild animals in specific soil areas.

But only slowly are we cataloging enough influences by the soil fertility on animal nutrition to catch a glimpse of the possibilities of growing healthy animals by more attention to management of the fertility of the soil with that objective as well as significant yields of crop mass per acre in mind. Perhaps we will have to wait for another centennial before enough facts about fertile soils as the basis of healthy animals can be catalogued to give us emphasis on the prevention of animal diseases via a few elements of soil origin for proper nutrition in place of cure and relief via myriads of drugs.

CHAPTER 10

Feed Efficiency
in Terms of Biological
Assays of Soil Treatments

THE RELATIONSHIP BETWEEN the distribution of livestock and fertility of soils is well defined. Throughout the United States the livestock population is largest in areas of high soil fertility. As the soil productivity declines in humid regions, the problems of keeping livestock thrifty and profitable have increased. Losses from bacterial and virus diseases are not as great as in past decades. However, despite extensive breed improvement, increased knowledge of production, and better equipment, nutritional diseases have not diminished, nor has the percentage of young that are saved kept pace with improved livestock practices. More problems are constantly presenting themselves. It is not unreasonable to believe that the feed crops on depleted soils may not be as nutritious as when soils were more productive and that some of the present animal production problems may be traced to the low quality of feeds now being used.

Chemical Composition & Nutritive Value
of Forages Influenced by Soil Type and Soil Treatment

Reports from most of the experiment stations in the eastern half of the United States show that the use of commercial fertilizers for the addition to the soil of deficient elements may increase, may decrease, or may have little effect on the concentration within the plant tissue of the added elements. These variations are often explained, for fields with mixed herbage or in pastures, on the basis of the changes in kind of plant that may be brought into dominance by the treatment. Nevertheless, these soil treatments may bring about variation in content of protein, minerals, or fiber within a single plant species. The extent of variation in chemical composition is influenced by any particular nutrient excess in the soil, and by the greater or lesser demands by the plant on nutrient elements coming from the soil.

It has been shown that plants produced on soils having a deficiency of one or more nutrients are of lower biological value to animals than are those where these elements are not lacking. Digestion trials have shown that the feed efficiencies and utilization of minerals vary widely for forages produced on different soils. These digestion differences cannot be correlated exactly with analyses of the feeds as commonly determined. Crampton and Maynard have pointed to the relationship between the lignin content of feeds and their utilization by animals.

Data showing the effect of soil treatments on the vitamin content of crops are none too consistent. It is probable that methods and technics in making analyses are not yet sufficiently standardized for reproducible results in the hands of different analysts. However, many of the data indicate that where crops are grown on soils containing a well balanced supply of plant nutrients or where conditions are optimum for plant growth, the vitamin content will be amply high.

If crops are of low nutrient value when grown on soils where certain elements are deficient, it is also probable that those forages containing unduly high percentages of these elements would be unbalanced, low in other elements, and of lower nutrient value than where all elements are present in more nearly balanced amounts. The excessive use of a single element fertilizer, or of unbalanced fertilizers on crops, may result in plants of as low biological value as those produced with a deficiency of the same element.

Animals Show Feed Efficiencies Related to Soil Treatment

Forages Influence Rate of Gain & Physiology of Lambs

In a continuation of work reported previously in which lespedeza hays from the same soil given different soil treatments were fed to feeder lambs, a wide variation in nutrient efficiency was obtained, as is shown in Table 1.

If the mean figure of the 3 years for the lespedeza is calculated, a ton of the hay receiving only phosphate with grain supplement is found to produce 128 pounds of animal gain, while a ton of hay from the soil receiving lime

Table 1

Lespedeza and Soybean Hays Required to Produce 1 Pound of Lamb Gain when Grown on Putnam Silt Loam Soil Receiving Different Soil Treatments. *

Year	Hay	Soil treatment		
		None	Phosphate	Lime + Phosphate
1939	Lespedeza	—	29.2	19.4
1940	Lespedeza	—	14.2	12.6
1941	Lespedeza	12.7†	9.7	7.6
1941	Soybean	9.7†	5.4	4.4

* Assuming all gain was made from hay, all animals received $\frac{1}{4}$ pound of shelled oats and $\frac{1}{4}$ pound of wheat bran daily. Each figure is average results from 7 to 12 lambs in each pen. Number varied in different years.
† No treatment; hay fed in 1941 only.

and phosphate would produce 164 pounds of gain, or an increased gain of nearly 44%.[1] The average yield of lespedeza hay for 3 years from the soil receiving phosphate was 2,120 pounds, while on the land where lime had been applied in addition to the phosphate the yield was 2,770 pounds. This is a difference in crop yield of 26%. However, when the hay corresponding to 1 acre of the phosphated land was fed to sheep, it produced a gain of 136 pounds, while the hay from 1 acre of the limed and phosphated land produced 227 pounds of gain. This is a difference in returns per acre of 67%.

Efficiency of Grain Utilization Affected

Not only has the hay grown on the treated soil given greater animal gain than the difference in tonnage yields would indicate, but the quantity of grain consumed for each pound of gain was widely different.

The figures given in Table 2 show that even though animals are fed the same amount of grain from the same source, the quantity required to produce a unit of gain can be much influenced by the kind of forage which it supplements. As an average of the figures for lespedeza hay, 4.6 pounds of grain were consumed for each pound of animal gain for the animals fed hay from the soil receiving only phosphate. Those fed the hay from land receiving both lime and phosphate consumed only 3.34 pounds of grain for each pound of gain. Thus, the hay from the land receiving only phosphate required over a third more grain to produce the same amount of gain

[1] Assuming all gains were made from hay as all animals received the same amount of grain.

Table 2

Grain Supplement Consumed Per Pound of Gain by Lambs Fed Lespedeza and Soybean Hays Grown on Differently Treated Soils.

Year	Hay	Soil treatment		
		None	Phosphate	Lime and phosphate
1939	Lespedeza	—	6.8	4.5
1940	Lespedeza	—	3.5	3.0
1941	Lespedeza	4.3	3.5	2.5
1941	Soybean	4.2	2.3	1.7

than did the hay from land receiving both lime and phosphorus. In terms of a practical farm viewpoint where it is assumed cheap forage is available and where grain is purchased, it would require 4,600 pounds of grain to produce a thousand pounds of lamb gain if the animals had free access to the phosphated hay, but only 3,340 pounds of grain if the animals had access to the hay grown on the soil treated with lime and phosphate.

Animal Appearance Reflects Effects of Soil Treatment

The lambs were vigorous at all times in all of the trials using the lespedeza and soybean hays. The only noticeable difference in the animals was in the appearance of the wool and its yolk content. In every trial the lambs on the hay from limed and phosphated soil were much dirtier, more shaggy, and rougher in appearance. On parting the wool, a large amount of yolk gave it a deeper yellow color. In contrast, the animals fed either the hay with no treatment or with phosphate were clean and smooth in appearance, while the wool was much whiter and contained less yolk. The lambs shown in Fig. 1 are representatives of the groups fed in the four trials.

Analyses of the wool showed that the fleeces from the sheep receiving the limed hay contained 2% more fat than those receiving the phosphated hay. When the wools were scoured with a 1% solution of potassium hydroxide, that from the lambs receiving only phosphated hay was attacked and lost 34% of its weight, while the wools from the lambs receiving the limed and phosphated hay remained fluffy and lost only 24%.

Evidently the wool from the lambs on the limed and phosphated hay had a different composition or had a thicker protective coating of fat and yolk which prevented it from heavy attack by the alkali. Regardless of the chemical or physical differences in the wools, it is significant that a simple treatment applied to the soil has not only been reflected in increased yield of forage, but when fed to sheep has brought about differences in rate of gain and altered the physiology of the animals sufficiently to be observed in the appearance and quality of the wool.

Feed Efficiency Reduced by Unbalanced Soil Treatments

In view of differences in the biological value of forages obtained in bioassays with sheep and the similar results obtained with rabbits, numerous bioassays have been made with rabbits of both forages and grains grown on various experimental fields of Missouri. The procedure followed was similar to that used by Crampton where uniform young

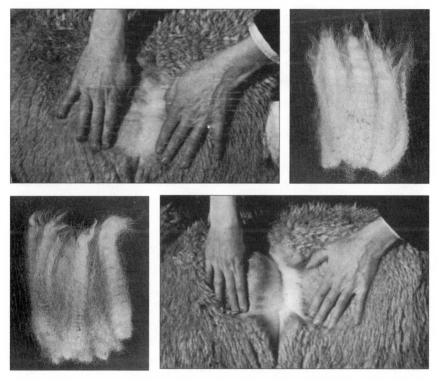

Fig. 1. Differences in wool as related to the forage from different soil treatments. Above, little yolk, white fibers, and smooth top of sheep from lespedeza with phosphate applied to the soil. Below, much yolk, yellow fibers, and rough top of sheep from lespedeza with lime plus phosphate applied to the soil.

rabbits were fed in screen-floored pens with facilities for collecting urine and feces. The animals were given *ad libitum* of the feed under test, and a constant amount of grain or hay supplements when they would not grow satisfactorily on the feeds under test alone. All animals were given distilled water and common salt. By keeping records of feed given and refused, the amount consumed was obtained; the digestibility was obtained from analyses of the feeds, feces, and urine; and the comparative efficiency of the feed in producing animal gain was determined.

Many of the assays made to date have been of an exploratory nature. Results have varied, depending on the soil type, season, and other factors. Nevertheless, these feeding and digestion trials show that the use of a soil treatment can alter the value of the plant as animal feed. It is significant, and somewhat surprising, that some of the soil treatments which have given maximum increases in yield in the field, particularly when the soil treatments were not considered as balanced, have produced crops of lower biological value than those from soils having received no treatment. It is also evident that the correlation between standard feed or mineral analyses and digestibility, or some animal response, are not so specifically related that these analyses can be used to forecast the value of a particular feed.

Nitrogen in Excess Reduces Feed Efficiency of Timothy

Pure stands of timothy[2] produced on a meadow fertilization experiment at Columbia, Mo., were fed to young rabbits for a period of 112 days. These animals were fed all the hay they would consume plus a constant daily feed of oats. The data in Table 3 give the analyses of these hays and the gains made by the animals.

All of these hays were of good quality. That receiving the sodium nitrate was much coarser and of a darker green color. The mineral analyses show that where nitrogen was applied, the percentages of phosphorus and calcium in the hay were lower than in the untreated hay. With the exception of the hay receiving nitrate of soda, the protein content in any of the hays receiving soil treatment was no higher than in the untreated. This would indicate that the increased growth compensated for the increased absorption of these nutrients.

---

[2] *None of the hays fed contained over 5% of other species than timothy.*

The animals receiving the sodium nitrate hay ate a greater amount per day and produced a more rapid gain than those given the untreated hay (Fig. 2) or those receiving the ammonium sulfate treated hay. However, when the gains are expressed on a basis of gain per unit of hay consumed, the efficiency was lower than on any of the other hays. The higher biological assay of the complete treatment hay over the others shows its higher nutritive value, although this difference would not be expected from the appearance of the hay or from the chemical analyses.

It is probable that the use of nitrogen alone on this phosphorus and calcium deficient soil furthered an already unbalanced soil condition resulting in abnormal plant metabolism and a forage of low quality. As a practical farm consideration, it would be a gross error to interpret the value of treatments on this soil, measured by their influence on the yield of timothy as a corresponding measure of the animal gains they would produce.

Deficiency of Potash Produces Forage of Low Nutrient Value

Rabbits were fed soybean hay produced on Putnam silt loam where various soil treatments had been used. An extreme potash deficiency had developed where limestone had been applied for some time. There was no evidence of potash deficiency on the unlimed soil.

The hays with no treatment and with no lime contained considerably more grass than the limed hay. The hays were chopped and the animals given all they would eat plus a small daily supplement of shelled oats.

The data given in Table 4 and Fig. 3, show that, although these differently treated hays vary little in nitrogen, phosphorus, and calcium contents, the hay from the plot receiving lime and phosphate and showing extreme potash deficiency was inferior as feed. There was a marked difference in animal gain caused by this one hay as compared to all the others. The hays from plots which received phosphate and potash and lime, phosphate, and potash produced the most rapid and efficient gains. All of these differences cannot be attributed to the effect of potash alone on the soybean plants since the untreated hay and that which received only phosphate contained considerably more grass than did the others. It is significant, however, that even though the hay receiving lime and phosphate and showing the extreme potash deficiency was practically pure soybeans, it was definitely inferior to the other hay con-

Table 3

Relation of Chemical Composition of Timothy Hay (1941 Crop) to Gains of Rabbits.

Soil treatment	Yield, lbs. per acre	Nitrogen		Ca, %	P, %	Grams gain in 112 days	Hay consumed per gram of gain*	Grain consumed per gram of gain
		Total, %	Water-soluble, %					
None................	1,745	1.12	0.16	0.49	0.142	721	11.6	2.6
Ammonium sulfate, 100 lbs. per acre in March	2,894	1.06	0.12	0.34	0.124	553	12.7	3.3
Sodium nitrate, 100 lbs. per acre in March. Sodium nitrate, 100 lbs. per acre in May..............	3,250	1.64	0.20	0.46	0.110	778	14.3	2.5
Complete†............	2,524	0.98	0.10	0.41	0.217	1,039	7.6	1.8

*Assuming all gain was made from hay. The grain ration was constant for all years.
†Limestone at 2½ tons in 1937, 100 lbs. of ammonium sulfate annually, 200 lbs. superphosphate and 50 lbs. KCl per acre in alternate years. (Applied in 1941.)

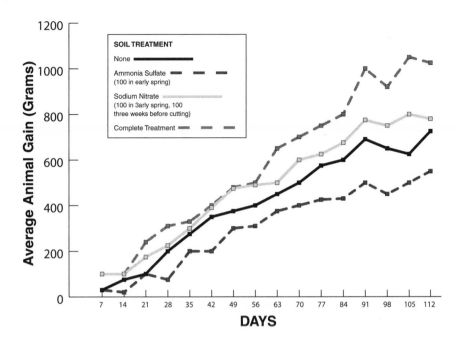

Fig. 2. Rates of gain for rabbits fed timothy hays grown on Putnam silt loam given different soil treatments. Average of three animals fed each hay.

Table 4

Relation of Chemical Composition of Soybean Hays to Gains of Rabbits.*

Soil treatment	Yield in lbs. per acre	N, %	P, %	Ca, %	Average gain in grams, 49 days
None......................	2,780	2.35	0.217	1.31	296
0-20-0, 150 lbs..........	2,500	2.15	0.240	1.28	229
0-20-10, 150 lbs	3,800	2.50	0.232	1.35	352
0-20-0, 150 lbs. plus† limestone	2,940	2.78	0.260	1.07	88
0-20-10, 150 lbs. plus limestone	3,800	2.92	0.262	1.28	363

*One year rotation of barley and soybeans. Fertilizers applied only to barley.
† Extreme potash deficiency.

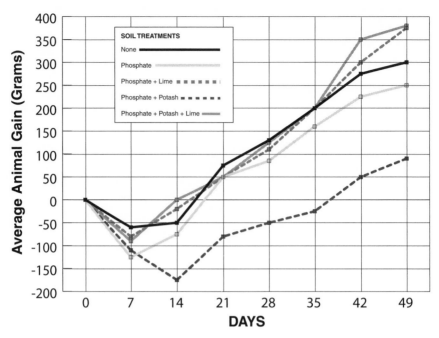

Fig. 3. Rates of gain for rabbits fed soybean hays grown on Putnam silt loam given different soil treatments. Average of three animals fed each hay.

taining some less nutritious species. From a practical standpoint, yield would be a poor index of the monetary returns that would be obtained from soil treatments when the hay is marketed through animals.

These animal gains indicate that when the potash became a limiting element, the physiology of the soybean plants was altered. The low content of calcium in the potash-deficient beans, which was the lowest for all hays despite the fact the soil had been limed, might indicate the inability of the limed plants to take up certain nutrients. It is possible that the physiological processes within the plant were so altered by the deficiency of potassium that organic compounds essential in the growth and development of the young animals were not produced by the plant. If they were, they were not digested, because the animals fed the hay from the soil receiving 0-20-10 made practically the same gain as those receiving the hay that received lime in addition. The latter might have been somewhat deficient in potassium (no fertilizer applied with soybeans) even though no plant deficiency symptoms were observed. If this was the case, then this deficiency would tend to reduce the hay quality but to a lesser degree than where the potash deficiency was evident. This would account for the small benefit from the limestone in contrast to the results with sheep on hays where no potash deficiency symptoms were observed. It is also probable that the calcium added to the soil by the fertilizer alone on the plot receiving only 0-20-10 was sufficient to supply the needs of the soybean (calcium content of this hay was highest of any fed) and these plants were growing on a more balanced supply of plant nutrients than where heavy applications of lime were made. If this is true, then it would appear that the application of calcium (or other elements) in excessive quantities without regard for the balance of other essential nutrients might produce crops of lower nutrient value than where no application of any kind was made.

Biological Value of Alfalfa Influenced by Soil Treatment

Alfalfa hay produced on Marshall silt loam, a soil of high fertility level, was fed to rabbits for two successive years. The hay yields were more than a ton and a half per acre on the untreated soil in 1940, the first year after seeding, and over 3 tons in 1941. There resulted a substantial yield response, nevertheless, to both lime and phosphorus. Analyses of the hays, whether from treated or untreated soil, show that these did not differ widely, except that the hay from the land receiving the heaviest application rate of phosphate had the highest concentration of phosphorus and of protein. This same hay also had the lowest calcium concentration, but there was little difference in percentage of calcium between any of the hays and the percentage figure for the no-treatment hay was almost as high as that of those hays receiving lime.

The first feeding trials with alfalfa were made in 1940. Nothing but hay, salt, and distilled water was fed to the animals at the outset of this first trial. Gains were so erratic that a supplement of corn was added to all pens. The hay from the untreated soil had the finest stems and the rabbits consumed it with the least waste. That from the plot with heavy phosphate was coarsest and much of it was refused. The gains were for only three animals on each hay in 1940 (Table 5) but serve, nevertheless, to point to the low feeding value of the hay receiving the large amount of phosphate.

In the trial with the hay grown in 1941, a larger number of animals (nine on each treatment) was used. They were given a constant amount of corn with the hay. Animal gains were much more consistent, as shown in Fig. 4. The hay receiving heavy applications of phosphate produced better gains than did the hays with lighter applications of phosphorus. This is the

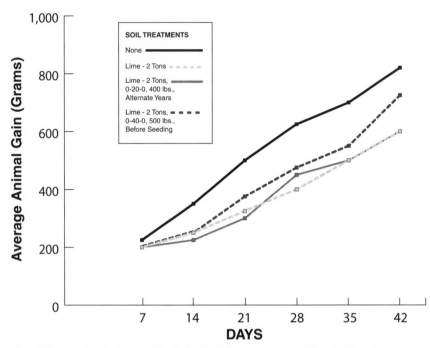

Fig. 4. Rates of gain for rabbits fed alfalfa hays grown on Marshall silt loam given different soil treatments. Average of nine animals fed each hay.

reverse of the results obtained in 1940. However, in 1941 both of the hays receiving phosphate were inferior to that from untreated soil when considered in terms of the rate of animal gain. The hay from the untreated soil again had finer stems than the hays from land receiving phosphate.

It is possible that the plants in 1940 from land receiving 500 pounds of 40% phosphate had an abnormal metabolism because of the excess of available phosphorus in relation to other elements. This possibly produced a feed of lower biochemical value under the assay conditions followed than that from the plants receiving only 400 pounds of 20% phosphate. The hay grown on the land in 1941 where the lesser amount of phosphorus was put on 2 years preceding may not have obtained sufficient phosphorus for optimum nutrient value, while the hay grown in 1941 where the heavier amount of phosphorus was applied in the fall of 1939 was probably no longer suffering from an excessive amount of phosphorus which may have been fixed in the soil by 1941 and partially removed by the previous year's crop. Further, it seems possible that the addition of lime alone may have magnified the phosphorus, or other nutrient, shortage in the alfalfa and

Table 5

Gains by Rabbits Fed Alfalfa Hay Produced Under Different Soil Treatments on Marshall Silt Loam.*

	1940 crops		1941 crops	
Soil treatments	Yield, lbs. per acre	Average gain, grams in 49 days†	Yield, lbs. per acre	Average gain, grams in 49 days‡
None........................	3,300	502	6,623	816
Limestone, 2 tons........	4,170	692	8,470	608
Limestone, 2 tons 0-20-0, 400 lbs. §.....	4,220	636	7,820	619
Limestone, 2 tons 0-40-0, 500 lbs.**........	6,290	571	9,120	732

* Alfalfa was seeded in the fall of 1939.
† Average of three animals.
‡ Average of nine animals.
§ Phosphate applied in alternate years.
**Phosphate (T.V.A.) applied only before seeding.

may have produced a feed of inferior quality as evidenced by the slower rate of rabbit gain for 1941. There is in these data an indication that soil treatments producing a maximum crop yield will not necessarily give highest feeding value if some essentials for crop growth are present in the treatment in excessive or deficient amounts.

Biochemical Values of Grains Differ

Soil treatments have much less effect on changing the mineral and protein content of grains than of forages. However, soil treatments have influenced the biochemical value of grains. Animals have shown a distinct preference for grains grown under balanced nutrient conditions. Feed efficiency, as measured by rabbit growth, has varied widely, depending on the soil treatment.

It has been difficult to obtain consistent differences through biological assays in grains produced on the same soil given different fertilizer treatments. The differences between grains are not as great as between forages and the experimental animal error is large in contrast to the possible differences

Table 6

Gains Made by Rabbits in 42 Days on Kafir Grain Produced in 1940 on Clarksville Gravelly Loam With Different Soil Treatments.

Soil treatment	Rabbit gain, grams	Grain yield, bu. per acre
None	789	11.5
Limestone, 2 tons 0-20-0, 150 lbs	741	20.0
Limestone, 2 tons 10-20-20, 150 lbs	654	28.0

between the grains. However, in some biological assays which are typical of a number that have been made, some of the soil treatments giving the highest bushel yields of grain have failed to give as satisfactory animal gains per unit of feed as have some of the soil treatments producing lower grain yields.

Kafir Quality Altered by Soil Treatment

Kafir grain produced on Clarksville gravelly loam in the Missouri Ozarks was fed to rabbits. The data given in Table 6 are an average of two feeding trials of the grain produced in the same season. The figures for gain are the means for six animals. In each case the animals were given free access to the grain and were given a supplement of mature bluegrass hay of poor quality, salt and distilled water.

That the efficiency of the grain should be lower as there were increasing soil treatments and decidedly increasing yields per acre is quite the unexpected. The results of the second trial confirmed those of the first.

The soil where this kafir was grown is low in organic matter and will give for most crops increases in yield from nitrogen, phosphorus, and lime but not from potash until after being limed for some years. No minor element deficiency symptoms in plants have been observed.

The kafir used in this feeding trial followed a crop of sweet clover plowed under as a green manure. It is possible that the addition of the nitrogen in the fertilizer plus the amount added in the sweet clover may have supplied an excess of nitrogen in relation to other elements, resulting in changed composition of the grain that was reflected in poorer utilization from the land receiving the 10-20-20 fertilizer.

Table 7

Gains Made by Rabbits in 84 Days on Corn from Soils Receiving Different Treatments.

Soil treatment and cropping system	Rabbit gain, grams in 84 days	Yield, bu. per acre
3-year rotation corn, wheat, red clover; no treatment for 50 years.....................	679	40.0
3-year rotation corn, wheat, red clover, manure, 6 tons per acre, 1888-28; since 1928, lime, 2 tons, 0-16-0, 200 lbs. on corn and wheat.................................	655	58.5
Corn, wheat; manure, 8 tons on corn	836	40.0
Corn, wheat, sweet clover (under); 0-10-10, 400 lbs. on corn and wheat	640	65.8

Feeding Efficiency of Corn Grain Altered by Soil Treatments

Four lots of corn produced on Putnam silt loam were fed to rabbits. The results obtained (Table 7), involving three animals on each grain, are typical of a number of trials with corn. They agree with the responses to the grain of kafir. In the first feeding it was difficult to keep the animals alive on the grain produced on the land where sweet clover had been turned under. The data are omitted. The grain was ground finely and kept before the animals at all times. In addition they were fed mature bluegrass hay.

The differences in nutritive value of these corn grains are evident. In these tests, as well as in other trials, difficulty was encountered in keeping the animals thrifty on grain produced on a soil high in nitrogen, especially when there were no additions of phosphorus or potash to the soil. From the poorer animal gains made on the grain following sweet clover, it appears that a level of active soil nitrogen too high in contrast to other elements, may produce grain of inferior feeding quality under the feeding plan followed. Grain produced under these high nitrogen conditions may be changed in its nutrient value sufficiently that it would need a different supplement for most efficient animal utilization.

Table 8

Relative Hardness of Corn Grains Grown on Soil Receiving Different Treatments in a Rotation of Corn and Wheat.

Soil treatment	Relative hardness*
None..	16.4
0-10-10, 400 lbs. on corn and wheat....................................	15.8
Manure, 8 tons on corn..	18.0
Manure, 8 tons on corn; 0-10-10, 400 lbs. on corn and wheat...	17.0
Sweet clover under ahead of corn......................................	20.0
Sweet clover under ahead of corn; 0-10-10, 400 lbs. on corn and wheat...	15.5

Determined by force required to push a 15° point, 2 mm in diameter, into the endosperm.

Animal Preference & Hardness of Grain Indicate Variability of Grains

A further suggestion of the difference in grain properties brought about by soil treatments is shown by animal preference trials and hardness tests. Corn was fed finely ground, cracked, and shelled under conditions giving the animals free choice. Usually, when the grains were fed whole or only cracked, the animals showed a preference for the softer corn. When they were finely ground, this difference in choice was largely eliminated and in some cases even reversed. The animal choice may differ if a protein supplement is given. In the preference trials with pigs, hardness seemed to be the primary factor in determining their choice. Soil treatments influenced the hardness of the corn grain as shown by a number of tests on corn grown under different soil fertility conditions. The results given in Table 8 are typical of the effect of different soil treatments on the relative hardness of the grain.

It is significant that manure increased the hardness of corn and that it was made still harder where sweet clover had been turned under. The addition of phosphorus and potash in all cases made the grain softer than it was on the comparison plot receiving no fertilizer. It appears that high fertility levels are conducive to the production of hard grain and that the grain is most resistant to breakage when grown on soil in which the nitrogen is particularly high in relation to the mineral elements. Regardless of animal choice or animal gain, it is not unreasonable to believe that corn grains of different hardness would contain different chemical compounds and that they might have different biological values, or influences, on the animals consuming them.

In animal preference trials with oats, wheat, and forages, where hardness could not be a factor, there were distinct animal choices for grain produced under certain conditions. Usually the grains preferred were those produced on soils of balanced fertility treatments rather than on those where one nutrient element may have been excessively high or low. In many cases animals showed a distinct preference for the grain from soil receiving a moderate fertilizer treatment rather than from those treatments where some element was excessively high, although the soil was producing the highest yield.

Discussion & Summary

Results of most agronomic researches are measured in terms of increased yields as bushels or tonnage of crops per acre. Biological assays now point out that these measures may not be accurate when agronomic products are to render their service in sustenance for animals. The values of improved varieties, of fertilizer treatments, of rotations, or soil management practices are based primarily on the number of bushels or pounds as increase over others that will be produced during a period of years by a new variety or practice. Other visible factors, such as quality, resistance to disease, and drought resistance, have been considered of secondary importance. Little or no attention has been given to chemical differences in the feeds or foods caused by different agronomic changes that could profoundly influence the animals and humans that consume these plant products.

The data of animal gains presented herewith demonstrate that forages and grains from the same soil given different treatments have varied widely in their capacities to produce animal gain. When the chemical composition of the feeds was changed by the different soil treatments, the animal response was not correlated closely enough to warrant the acceptance of the chemical analyses as an index of nutritive value. There is the strong suggestion that differences in feeds are brought about by soil treatments other than those commonly measured by standard methods of feed analyses. Only through assays with animals can these differences be determined.

On a soil low in lime and phosphorus, addition of phosphorus alone increased the efficiency of forage when fed to lambs. When limestone was added in addition to the phosphate, the nutritive value of the hays was further improved. Differences in the amount of improvement due to the different soil treatments varied from year to year. However, the relationship with reference to soil treatment held true in all trials. It appears that nutritional differences were greatest in seasons unfavorable for plant growth. The protein and mineral contents of these hays did not differ as widely as their efficiencies in producing animal gain. This would indicate that the soil treatments brought about other composition changes not commonly measured. The animals made more gain from each unit of grain consumed as a supplement to the phosphated hay than to the untreated hays, and those fed hay from the soil receiving lime and phosphate made more gain on the grain consumed than did those receiving hay from the land where only phosphate had been applied. All animals fed on the hay from the soil receiving both lime and phosphate had a higher oil and yolk content. There was a significant difference in the nitrogen, sulfur, and phosphorus contents of the wool. Further differences were obtained when the wool was scoured by means of alkali. In the alkali solution the wool from the lambs fed the phosphated hay decomposed while that from the soil receiving both lime and phosphate retained its luster and carded out to give customary fluffiness. It is significant that a simple treatment applied to the soil changed the composition of plants, altered the physiology of animals consuming the hay, and affected the appearance and properties of the wool. Since the wool qualities were changed by soil treatments, it is not unreasonable to assume that other body processes could have been altered so as to affect profoundly the metabolic and reproductive processes in the animals.

The addition of any plant nutrient to a soil without regard to the amount applied as related to the kind and supply of the nutrients in the soil may not always give feed of improved nutritive value. Evidence is presented where the addition of fertilizer or lime brought about an unbalanced nutrient condition in the soil which actually resulted in crops of lower efficiency than where no nutrient additions were made.

Timothy hay grown on soil having an excess of nitrogen, alfalfa with an excess of lime or phosphorus, and soybeans grown on a soil made deficient in potash through excessive applications of lime have all been lower in nutritive value than where no soil treatments were added. However, when these treatments were balanced by the addition of other plant nutrients, the quality of the feed was improved over that from the untreated soil. These results would indicate that tonnage yields are not a complete measure of the value of soil treatment and that maximum feeding value of forages can be obtained only when all soil nutrients are present in the proper ratios.

Since grains are only produced by crops after vegetative growth has been completed, the composition can not be altered as much by soil treatments as can that of forages. Nevertheless, the effect of soil treatments on the nutritive quality of grains was demonstrated. Trails with kafir and corn showed that the nutritive values of these grains produced on poor soils may be improved by addition of moderate amounts of the deficient elements. However, when some elements are added in excessive quantities, the nutritive value may be reduced below that of the untreated grains. Pressure tests have shown that the hardness of corn may be markedly influenced by soil treatment. It is not unreasonable to assume that grains varying in hardness will contain different organic compounds that may have a different effect on animal metabolism.

When animals were given a chance to show preference for grains from differently treated soil, wide variations in choice were found. In corn, hardness is one of the principal factors observed to influence choice. However, with such grains as oats and wheat the preference of animals for the grain from a particular soil treatment can only be attributed to chemical properties.

These results all point to differences in the value of plants as animal feed brought about by soil treatments, and that there are other differences in these plant products than are commonly determined by standard feed analyses. It has been well established that lignin accumulates within the plant when some growth factor, such as climate, or lack of fertility produces slow growth of plants. It is possible that this material could prevent the animal's digestive juices from attacking the cell contents and that the feed would pass through the animals undigested.

The functions of the different nutrients in plant metabolism are not well known. Where deficiencies exist, it is possible that some organic compounds, highly essential in animal growth, might not be synthesized within the plant and thus result in a feed of lower nutritive value. Since all results indicate that feeds produced under well-balanced fertility conditions are usually most effectively utilized by animals, it is not unreasonable to believe that an excess of some element might also prevent the synthesis of these compounds essential for animal growth, or that it might cause compounds to be formed that would be injurious.

All of these results point to the necessity of knowing the fertility properties of individual soils. If nutritious feeds are to be produced for animal and human consumption, then the soil on which they are grown must contain not only all the proper elements for plant growth, but these must be presented by the soil in proper ratios. It is only through proper and intelligent management that farm acres can be made to produce high yields of quality products. On soils of low productive capacity, the soil treatment can be expected to give benefits in addition to those of merely increasing the tonnage yields. The full value of these treatments, however, cannot be measured as yet without the use of animal assay.

CHAPTER 11

Taking Our Soils for Granted

BECAUSE SOILS SEEM to be everywhere and because plants with their roots in the earth are all about us, we take soils and crops on them all for granted. But now that there is no more "new land" available, and food shortages are bringing our attention "back to the soil," we are beginning to see that we cannot continue to take our soils for granted. We are even concerned about soil conservation.

Man, at the top of the pyramid of all the different life forms, has the help of many of these in reaching out over extensive areas of soil to collect his essential food elements. There are some dozen different chemical elements coming directly from the soil. Man himself travels far to eat the fruits of many different soils.

Then, too, he is omnivorous, that is, he eats most everything including vegetable, animal and even mineral, to increase the possibilities of giving his body the essential elements found in the soil. Four of these come from the air and water, compounded by sunshine. Thus plants send their roots searching through the soils, collecting and fabricating man's foods. Animals search through the plants to collect and construct still further. And man himself selects from all these—both plants and animals—the bulk and concentrates he needs for energy, growth, reproduction, and other complicated body functions.

All these performances and body processes are too often taken for granted and with no recognition of the soil as a helper or a hindrance. We have seemingly been far removed from the soil. Nevertheless, the changing conditions in economics, in agricultural production, in the capacity of our soils to provide essentials, and in the nutritive quality of our foods all bring us to think more about the soil.

If we should follow the suggestions of one of the American poets who said, "go forth unto the open sky and list to Nature's teachings," we can see that the wild animals—quite different from man—do not take their soils for granted.

The bison or buffalo was a critical examiner of his feed according to the soil growing it. In fact, he gave his name to "buffalo grass," the particular grass which the pioneers listed as his choice. Buffalo grass and the range of the buffalo did not extend very widely. The densest population of these brawny animals covered a limited climatic area of small extent from East to West though much more extensive from North to South.

The fertility of particular soils limited the territory over which the buffalo roamed. The climate, as it left more lime and other nutrients in the surface soil near the grass roots, controlled the buffalo range. Coincidentally, it is on these mineral-rich, less-leached soils under lower rainfall, or on these original buffalo soils, where our hard wheat of high protein and high mineral content grows today. It is also on these soils that cattle in large numbers literally raise themselves and the Herefords have made their reputation. It is these soils that produce, not tons per acre of woody vegetation, but short grass of extremely high nutritive quality.

The buffalo had sense enough to stay on his particular soils. He wasn't lured eastward to soils leached by higher rainfall nor to bluestem, bunch grass and other native vegetations yielding much higher tonnages per acre. There were no mountains, big rivers, or other land barriers to obstruct his travel eastward toward more woody vegetation.

As a strictly herbivorous feeder, his sense of better feed from more fertile soil kept him on the "buffalo grass" area and thereby on the soil quality that through this plant made him brawny, big of bone, and consequently King of the Plains. The buffalo knew his soils. He did not take them for granted.

Because we have been taking our soils for granted there are many instances to show that the soils have been going down in fertility while we have thought they are as good as when our fathers or grandfathers farmed them. Some illustrations from Missouri's many experienced cattle breeders may well serve.

A distinguished Hereford breeder, only recently deceased, accumulated a wealth of knowledge and sales experience with his choice breed during fifty years on the prairie soils of northeast Missouri. But to his disappointment in his later years he discovered that he had been oblivious to the fact that the soil of his extensive pastures had been going downward in supplies of minerals to give the former quality of feed. His calf crops were too low because the females were not reproducing regularly, regardless of attempts to provide better bulls.

Shy breeders were becoming more numerous. Good females were dropping out too early in their breeding life. Some with the best pedigrees were calving only in alternate years, and calves were coming at most any time instead of as one crop in the spring season, as Nature has most young animals come. Heifers were not the desirable thrifty animals, but of rounded backlines, tender pasterns, drooping heads, dull eyes, and other indications of low thrift even on pastures apparently lush in terms of abundant herbage.

On this farm the humus of the soil is no longer what it was fifty years ago when the breeding business in Herefords was coming up so well. The soil has weakened as the foundation on which both the breed and the breeder originally rose. It has grown old faster than the owner because it has given much of itself to the business but gotten none of the limestone, phosphate, green manures, and other fertilizer it should have had in return. It has been taken for granted too long. Now as it is passed on to the children—like so much other land—they may well say, "Yes, here is the farm, but what about the soil?"

Fortunately, this question has been answered by another and younger Hereford breeder who is succeeding today on the same soil type and using foundation stock purchased from the older breeder. This newer herd is under a breeder-farmer who will not take his soil for granted. Though much of the original surface soil on his farm had eroded away before he came into possession, he is rejuvenating the clay-points of subsoil and restoring the soil fertility on his farm by means of phosphates, limestone, and any possible fertilizers that will help make sod crops, to provide green manures, and give fertility features as supplements to contour cultivation on the dangerous slopes.

His herd of cattle, though started originally as a remnant of a declining one, is giving calf crops of almost 100 per cent. The calves all come within a limited period in the spring. The farm not only produces ample supply but also high quality feed. The soil under this rebuilding process has gone up to an alfalfa level while the Hereford herd has gone up to the blue ribbon level in the eyes of those who know cattle.

It is this breeder's belief that attention to his soil fertility reduces the attention needed by the cattle. "No," he will say, "we cannot take our soils for granted when they and their fertility are so basic to a type of agriculture that depends in a large measure on livestock."

Our human foods, too, have been taken for granted. We have measured them in terms of bulk rather than quality grown into them by the soil. Processing foods has taken out much that the soil and Nature's fabrication have put into them. Milk is measured by the volume or by the fat content. The former measures bulk and the latter mainly fuel value. Its measure in terms of growth quality for the young cannot be recorded by these measures. It must be scaled in terms of the soil.

The "town without a toothache" (Hereford, Texas) has suddenly become news, apparently because we had previously taken our soils for granted. We forget them as the basis of health. Likewise we had accepted bad teeth as though they were natural. Since bad teeth are but an exposed part of a bad skeleton we need to take seriously this demonstration that we all have been taking our bone troubles for granted.

We have failed to give attention to the soils from which must come the calcium and phosphorus needed to construct sound bones and good teeth. We forget that it is by means of soil fertility that Nature constructs the vitamins and other catalytic agencies that facilitate body growth and function. Human health too, depends on the soil, which, common as it is, is seemingly still too far removed from us to be so connected in our thinking.

Fertile virgin soils, plenty of land, and an abundance of humus and other fertility compounds were a natural inducement to mental lassitude. It bred indifference to erosion of the body of the soil, and exploitation of its stores of humus and fertility. But then the number of draftee rejections are so high in some soil areas, the national health pattern is beginning to delineate itself according to the soil's pattern of essentials for nourishing both beast and man.

Soil conservation is now taking a national inventory of the disappearing hidden qualities by which soils sustain domestic animal life at profitable economic levels and human life at high planes of good health and therefore of efficient citizenry. Our own future—but more particularly our place in the international future, points out forcefully that when our national health as well as our national wealth lies in our hands we cannot long continue to take our soils for granted.

CHAPTER 12

Biosynthesis of Amino Acids According to Soil Fertility, Timothy Hay Grown with Trace Elements

FOR THE SUCCESSFULL management of the production of feed and food, the fuller comprehension of the functions of the soil's inorganic elements catalyzing the synthesis, by plants, of the amino acids required by various forms of life is becoming more essential. The quality of food commodities relative to the proteins and protein-like substances has become a much more serious matter than their quantity.

The production of carbohydrates (or fats) as bulk by plants results readily from the growth of most any kinds of them. Such occurs on soils with less specific or complete arrays of the inorganic fertility supplies offered. But the synthesis by plants of the necessary amino acids, while guaranteeing both the quality and quantity of those in the daily protein required by warm-blooded animals and man, looms up as a most significant matter in the (a) choice of the crops with high potentialities for protein, and (b) management of the soil fertility (organic as well as inorganic) more completely supplied and more specifically balanced than we yet surmise.

Crude Protein may be all too "Crude"

Research along the above line of thinking is already supporting the validity of it. The list of essential inorganic elements is extending itself. It now includes many which were formerly neglected but unwittingly applied, such as sulfur and chlorine, and those needed only in trace amounts. Among the latter, more are becoming essentials according as refinements in chemical methods and bioassays classify them in that category. Boron, for example, suggests itself as an essential element for warm-blooded animals including man. Selenium and chromium have now been given functional essentiality, while cadmium has been found in conjunction with zinc in a protein fraction of horse kidney, given the name of metallothionein. Some experiments prompted the theory that a more fitting balance of the major nutrient elements in the soil for the plant's higher production of its required proteins may improve the root's activities in taking up the trace elements from the soil. It may also modify the catalytic services by the trace elements in the plant's synthesis of compounds essential in its own growth, protection and reproduction.

With nitrogen in commercial fertilizers going into such extensive use on non-legumes in the hope of higher concentrations of protein, resulting from it in the forages, there is the prevailing belief that the increase in crude protein (nitrogen multiplied by 6.25) must represent higher quality as feed. More of protein so obtained and classified may be making it all the more crude and even dangerously so.

Some Observations

That such may be the fact was demonstrated by the death of cattle consuming the fodder from corn (maize) in 1954 when the drought and the extreme temperatures (113°F) destroyed the enzymes in the bleached leaves (duplicating the pattern of nitrogen deficiency in the leaf) in Missouri (U.S.A.) in early July, which was the beginning of an extended, hot, dry season lasting well into September. In early August there was a rainfall of near two inches. Maize fodder cut and fed in July was not lethal to livestock. But that which was cut and fed in September was fatal with symptoms diagnosed as nitrite—nitrate poisoning. The filling of a silo at that season was fatal, because of the inhalation of nitrous fumes, to a workman entering after a night following the previous day's filling operation.

Chemical tests of the lower sections of the stalks of maize, injured by the drought, revealed as much as 0.65 per cent of nitrogen in the nitrite—nitrate forms in the dry matter when the combined total nitrogen in all forms was only 1.00 per cent. Were this amount of total nitrogen considered as 6.25 per cent crude protein of feed value, this would be far from the truth when by that mathematical evaluation the fodder contained 4.06 per cent of poisons (0.65 times 6.25 = 4.06).

Timothy (*Phleum pratense*) was once a prominent hay crop for horses in eastern United States. But it has been reported that proprietors of livery stables in earlier days learned that their horses fed on timothy hay fertilized with Chile saltpeters could not hold up under a long day's travel. Timothy was feed also for other farm animals, especially when grown with red clover, which crop combination was once an extensive one in farm practice.

With the dwindling acreage given to red clover because of costly seed and numerous failures of seedlings without careful soil treatments ahead of them, the question whether fertilization of timothy (and other non-legume forages) with nitrogen and other essentials including trace elements would improve its feeding value, was considered for test.

That timothy hay is not of the rabbits' choice equal to that of red clover hay was indicated in some bioassays of these two hays. It was observed that if one handled the red clover hay in the large room at some distance from the rabbit hutches, those animals responded immediately by moving to the empty hay racks on one side of them. But if one handled the timothy hay similarly, they remained indifferently quiet, regardless of the time period since the previous feeding. Since timothy is not of marked choice by this test animal, the question of whether the soil treatments might shift its rank upward in that category seemed a big one.

In applying commercial nitrogen in fertilizers more widely for non-legumes on our humid soils, we dare not assume the crop's synthesis of this element into crude protein, much less into an array of amino acids making complete proteins on the more highly developed soils. As agronomists fertilizing such soils for a grass agriculture, we need to appreciate the responsibility of providing a fertility balanced in all other respects before nitrogen is applied for the production of more protein in the crop to make more and better feed thereby.

Chemical Composition of Timothy Hays
Used in Bioassay

In some experiments studying the value of nitrogen as a soil treatment for possible improved feeding values in terms of the amino acids in a non-legume, some timothy was grown on Clarksville gravelly loam* with a basic treatment of limestone, phosphorus, and potassium over an area extensive enough to permit seven additional treatments of higher applications of nitrogen (40 pounds nitrogen per acre as initial fertilizer plus 60 pounds of it later as solutions) coupled separately with one of the five trace elements, namely boron, zinc, manganese, cobalt, and copper, and then also with all five of these trace elements in a mixture. Many of these salts were sulfates.

This is the upland soil of the Ozark area. It is a residual limestone soil with considerable cherty fragments scattered throughout. It is of low productivity, hence not cultivated but kept in grass.

The timothy hays were harvested by treated plots and put under chemical analyses of their ash for the elements, phosphorus, potassium, calcium, sulfur, magnesium, sodium, and also for the trace elements, manganese, iron, boron, zinc, and cobalt. The data are given in Table 1. These more complete inorganic analyses were made of the hays from the seven plots given the above heavier application of nitrogen and of those in combinations of the lesser amounts of nitrogen. It was the hays grown under these treatments which were put under careful bioassay later by feeding them to weanling rabbits. These timothy hays were analyzed also for their amino acid contents by microbiological procedures, according to modifications of the methods of Stokes *et al.* The results, tabulated in their relation to the total nitrogen are given in Table 2, for their respective contents of the ten essential amino acids.

Results

According to the data in the Table 2, the separate trace elements as soil treatments, save boron and cobalt, gave a lowered percentage of total nitrogen * in the dry matter, or thereby, a lower total crude protein. This might suggest a more efficient metabolic service for plant growth (as mass) by nitrogen in those three cases of the combination with manganese, zinc, and copper as soil treatments, that is, giving more plant growth per unit of nitrogen and of these fertility trace elements. Cobalt was without disturbing effect on the concentration of the total nitrogen in the timothy hay. Boron increased it by .13 per cent in the absolute, raising it from 1.34 to 1.47, or nearly ten per cent, relatively. The mixture of all five trace elements cannot be considered as a significant modifier of the concentration of the total nitrogen when this was increased only from 1.34 to 1.35 per cent. It is significant to note that the extra nitrogen applied to the soil pushed up the concentration of nitrogen in the dry matter of the timothy giving the percentage series of 0.91, 0.88, 1.02, and 1.34 for the series of applications of 0.0, 40., 70., and 100 pounds of this element per acre.

According to the influences of the trace elements supplementing the nitrogen as soil treatments, if one were to use these nitrogen values, the treatment with boron gave a crude protein content 24 per cent higher than that by the soil treatment of manganese comparatively, as 9.18 per cent and 7.18 per cent respectively. If the timothy hays are arranged in order of decreasing concentrations of crude protein for the respective soil

---

* Measured by modified Kjeldahl method in order to include nitrates.

Table 1

Inorganic Elements in Timothy Hay

Treatments (pounds per acre)	P%	Ca%	K%	Mg%	Na%	S%	Mn ppm	Fe ppm	B** ppm	Zn** ppm	Co** ppm
No Nitrogen	.175	.280	1.43	.210	.070	.146	147	355			
40 Nitrogen	.123	.217	1.18	.210	.045	.125	147	364			
40 Nitrogen + 30 N*	.129	.204	1.24	.268	.055	.127	134	295			
40 Nitrogen + 60 N***	.129	.187	1.16	.222	.045	.123	119	419	3.7	10.4	.06
40 Nitrogen + B	.128	.235	1.11	.275	.055	.128	134	345	5.5	4.8	.08
40 Nitrogen + Z	.120	.192	0.97	.262	.060	.150	60	295	5.2	20.8	.02
40 Nitrogen + Mn	.136	.193	1.08	.157	.050	.127	105	537	5.9	14.4	.08
40 Nitrogen + Co	.130	.221	1.03	.275	.050	.141	105	352	6.2	12.4	.03
40 Nitrogen + Cu	.130	.238	1.08	.281	.050	.142	105	337	6.0	22.4	.03
40 Nitrogen + the 5 trace elements	.152	.240	1.07	.238	.045	.130	60	375	5.9	32.8	.03
Mean Values	.133	.221	.113	.240	.052	.134	112	366	5.5	16.9	.047

*Extra nitrogen fertilizer was applied in the form of solution.

**Determined by spectrographic methods.

***This 60 N applied also with each trace element. See Table 3.

Table 2

Nitrogen (%) and Amino Acid Contents (Mg/g Dry Matter) of Timothy

Treatments (pounds per acre)	Nitrogen	Methionine	Tryptophane	Lysine	Threonine	Valine	Leucine	Isoleucine	Histidine	Arginine	Phenylalanine	Total amino acids
No Nitrogen	.915	.50	2.48	.715	2.60	2.86	12.1	6.35	.81	2.86	2.48	33.76
40 Nitrogen	.884	.39	2.16	.894	2.00	2.64	9.0	5.11	.65	2.68	2.02	27.55
40 Nitrogen + 30 N*	1.02	.35	2.24	1.20	2.40	2.76	11.5	5.58	.59	2.88	2.09	31.60
40 Nitrogen + 60 N**	1.34	.52	2.90	1.65	2.80	3.69	14.6	7.12	.91	3.75	2.95	40.90
40 Nitrogen + B***	1.47	.70	2.90	1.82	3.26	3.74	14.6	7.05	.80	4.00	2.80	41.67
40 Nitrogen + Zn	1.30	.56	2.86	1.58	3.04	3.23	13.2	7.13	.82	3.45	2.66	38.53
40 Nitrogen + Mn	1.15	.57	3.39	1.40	2.80	3.48	13.5	7.20	.67	3.88	2.81	39.70
40 Nitrogen + Co	1.34	.76	3.39	1.66	3.04	3.56	14.6	7.42	.89	3.88	2.86	42.06
40 Nitrogen + Cu	1.21	.45	2.73	1.68	2.78	3.12	14.2	6.62	.67	2.55	2.53	37.33
40 Nitrogen + the 5 trace elements	1.35	.72	3.61	1.84	3.06	3.59	13.6	7.31	.89	4.00	2.94	41.56

*Extra nitrogen fertilizer was applied in the form of solution.
**This 60 N was applied also with each trace element. See Table 3.
***Also 60 N with trace elements.

treatments, this order is quite different from that according to concentrations of the ten essential amino acids, set up for comparisons in Table 3. Also, if one compares the percentages of the dry matter made up of the ten essential amino acids—measured separately and in total—with the total nitrogen, it is interesting to note the variations in the mathematical factors by which the nitrogen would need to be multiplied to obtain the values of the ten essential amino acids combined. These values, or factors, varied from 3.45 for the soil treated with manganese, the trace element connected with the lowest crude protein, to 2.83 for boron connected with the highest crude protein in this series. This would suggest the lowest crude protein concentration as the most efficient in converting its nitrogen or itself into the ten essential amino acids.

Deaths from Heat Showed Proteins of Timothy not Equal to Other Proteins

That even such measures of the totals of the essential amino acids alone are not a true index of the nutritional value of the hay was shown in the feeding trials of these hays using weanling rabbits as the bioassay agents during the summer of 1954 which gave disastrous results in the deaths of them in connection with the heat wave of that unusual summer when the tests were made.

That timothy hay, even when fertilized with increasing amounts of nitrogen, is not taken so readily by rabbits was demonstrated in some preliminary trials. Given three hay samples representing fertilization with mounting increments of nitrogen, the rabbits chose hays with more nitrogen only at the beginning of the increased fertilization scale. They reversed this behavior, choosing hay with lesser amounts of applied nitrogen, at the higher increments of the fertilization scale. They exhibited reluctance to eat any grown with nitrogen fertilization at the largest increments applied.

In some additional trials with rabbits offered a constant amount of grain (maize) per day along with four separate lots of hay (fescue, *Festuca elatior* L var. *arundinacea*) given increasing nitrogen fertilization, the consumptions of the hays by these bioassayers of nutritional quality according to soil treatments put the amounts as ratios to grain in the following order as decreases for more nitrogen applied, namely, 1.93, 1.43, 1.16, and 1.00 by using the lowest ratio as 1.00. The amount of fescue hay per 20 rabbits per day as means of choices of 8 soil treatments was 168 g when for red clover for 4 treatments it was 840 g showing the former plant species one

Table 3

Timothy Hays Arranged in Order of Decreasing Nitrogen (Crude Protein) to Exhibit their Differing Orders (a) According to their Totals of the Ten Essential Amino Acids and (b) According to Arithmetical Factors by which Nitrogen must be Multiplied to Represent those Amino Acids

Soil treatments	Nitrogen*	Crude protein*	Acids*	Decreasing order	Factor**	Decreasing order
40 lbs N + 60 lbs N + Boron	1.47	9.187	4.167	2	2.83	7
40 lbs N + 60 lbs N + all 5 traces	1.35	8.437	4.156	3	3.07	4
40 lbs N + 60 lbs N	1.34	8.375	4.090	4	3.05	5
40 lbs N + 60 lbs N + Cobalt	1.34	8.375	4.206	1	3.13	2
40 lbs N + 60 lbs N + Zinc	1.30	8.125	3.853	6	2.96	6
40 lbs N + 60 lbs N + Copper	1.21	7.562	3.737	7	3.08	3
40 lbs N + 60 lbs N + Manganese	1.15	7.187	3.970	5	3.45	1

* As per cent of dry matter.
** Factor by which the nitrogen must be multiplied to give the total amounts of the amino acids listed.

of poor choice. It was more so when fertilized with increasing amounts of nitrogen. By using the test rabbits with the same maize and each of the hays separately, the first increment of nitrogen fertilization raised the amount taken but even that was less than of hay given less nitrogen coupled with phosphate fertilizers. Higher applications of nitrogen put the hay in choices below that of no nitrogen treatments.

When the first set of four separate soil treatments of increasing nitrogen fertilization under the fescue hay were submitted to the rabbits' choice, the daily consumptions per 20 rabbits varied from a low of 22.7 to a high of 44.5 g per soil treatment with a total of the four at 126.4. For the second set of four soil treatments of increasing nitrogen with some phosphate the daily consumptions varied from a low of 24.0 to a high of 85.4 g with a total of the four at 211 or a mean of the eight of 168.5 grams.

In corresponding trials with alfalfa hay, a legume, grown with increments of nitrogen fertilizers coupled with given amounts of phosphate and also limestone, the amounts consumed for the four soil treatments as ratios of hay to grain were 6.11, 5.42, 2.25, and 1.25 with the first choice of alfalfa being that grown without nitrogen fertilization. The amount of alfalfa hay consumed per 20 rabbits per day as the mean of choices of 8 soil treatments was 651.0 g.

For the first set of four choices the daily consumptions per treatment varied from a low of 51.6 to a high of 256.0 g per day per 20 rabbits with a total of the four at 622.9. For the second set the low was 68.5 and the high 297.2 while the total was 679.4 g.

For the choices of the red clover with but one set of four treatments other than mainly nitrogen, the low was 76.2 and the high 374.1 while the total was 840 g.

While the choice by the rabbits of the fescue hay was improved by the first increment of nitrogen to the soil growing it but was lowered by additional increments, any increment of nitrogen fertilizer for the alfalfa hay, a legume, lowered it in the choice by the rabbits. It is significant to note the differences in plant species and in the total amounts of hays taken, and also the changes in choice by the treatments of the soil growing either species.

Timothy hays grown on soils with different treatments fed to lambs over a winter period in some additional studies also showed the low feed values of the hays in the irregularities of the health of these animals. The lowest gains were recorded for the hay grown with only nitrogen as soil treatment. They exhibited increasing lameness first in one hind leg, then in both, then failing locomotion and later death. Irregular growths of the hoofs were commonly visible symptoms.

While timothy hay in combination with grain is not the animal's choice, yet if soil treatments using nitrogen in addition to basic other treatments including the trace elements, will improve the plant's production of proteins, it was deemed worthy of test of the protein values of timothy hay under such generous soil improvements.

When the tests using rabbits were set op for the summer of 1954, no record heat wave in Missouri, U.S.A., was anticipated. Nevertheless, while that disaster as deaths of the test animals upset the records of gains or losses in weights by them, it served in an unusual way to demonstrate the low value of the protein in the timothy species grown even under such supposedly complete soil treatments.

The mounting temperatures of the summer heat wave correlated themselves with the increasing number of deaths of the experimental rabbits fed on the lots of timothy hay combined in all cases with wheat of a single lot. There was no apparent correlation between the schedule of deaths and the soil treatments of the timothy hays. At the fortnightly weighing periods, the lots of rabbits were each restored to its initial numbers by adding individuals from the remaining original lot which suffered no heat fatalities. Those in the original lot, in the same location as the test rabbits, were fed on the same wheat grain, but this was combined with green grass growing on the nearby soil, fertilized and watered with the rabbit manure and hutch washings.

Deaths from the heat began on June 11 and amounted to a total of 57 (nearly 75%) for the seven lots by July 17, or the termination date set for the six-week trial. During the heat wave the maxima of temperatures ranged from 88° to 113°F with a mean maximum of 99.4°F during the fortnight closing with July 17.

On that day and forward (with one death the preceding night) the fatal ration of wheat and timothy hay was supplemented with 10 g per rabbit per day of commercial, fat-free, dried skim-milk powder. No more deaths occurred during the extension of the experiment for nine days, when the maximum daily temperatures ranged from 89° to 111°F with a mean maximum of 98.2°F.

As a sequel to the improved animal reactions to the high temperatures because of the extra protein supplied in the skim-milk powder, a repeat of the former test was started promptly on July 26 using maize, oats and the wheat in equal parts by weight, as the grain of the rations along with the roughages of the same timothy hays previously used. This trial, duplicating the preceding one and under the continuing high temperatures exhibited fatalities of the rabbits again until August 23 (during four weeks), when the feeding of the timothy hay was discontinued and red clover hay was fed instead.

No deaths of the experimental rabbits occurred during the extension of the test with the red clover hay for the fortnight from August 23 to September 6, during which the maxima of the continued high temperatures ranged from 79° to 102° with a mean maximum of 97.6°F for those 14 days. For the fortnight preceding the data of change to the red clover hay, the maxima ranged from 70° to 98°F, with a mean maximum of 82.5°F. At the close of this test with too many early disasters to give any reliable data as weights, there were still eight rabbits left of the original lot fed during the entire summer on the wheat-grass ration among which no fatalities had occurred during the extensive record-breaking heat wave.

Discussion

While the low values of crude protein in forages or hays can be improved by fertilizing the soil with nitrogen in conjunction with other elements, there is possible error in believing that such higher concentrations of total nitrogen in crops mean more protein either in quantity or quality.

In terms of the animal's choice, the non-legumes fertilized naturally by nitrogen in urinary and fecal droppings are refused as shown by the tall, green spots in pastures on humid soils. Self-restrictions of consumptions by the animals, ranging from 220 to 10 grams per day per rabbit, as the cited differences between fescue and alfalfa, militate against the animal's getting enough of the amino acids to provide the protein requirements when other factors than these protein parts seem to be responsible. Only the animal can be the final test of what the soil treatments do to make feeds of high quality as nutrition.

That feed values, according to soil treatments, need to be put under bioassay with more than animal survival and gain in weight as the criteria, was demonstrated by the accidental deaths of the rabbits at higher temperatures, but their survival on the same feed at lower ones. The former was a readily evident, clinical situation; the latter an undetected, subclinical one. What the level of health was of the latter remained unmeasured, though very probably a low one.

The chemical compositions as ash and as amino acids added themselves to the many tabulations of modified values of crops because of soil treatments with fertilizers. But they indicated no correlations of suggestive values, of possible help in the interpretation of the animals reactions to the feed, as growth, self-protection and reproduction. Perhaps with more biochemical values resulting from our relating the animal nutrition to the plant nutrition, and the latter in turn, to the soil fertility through bioassays, we may interpret the biosynthesis of amino acids by plants for wiser guidance of soil treatments accordingly.

Summary

Timothy hays grown with intensive soil treatments, including trace elements, (without significant differences in yields of hay per acre), were put under bioassay by weanling rabbits, only to have the high temperatures of a summer heat wave demonstrate by deaths of these test animals, regardless of soil treatments, that the protein intake (and what might accompany it) was not equal to the animal's needs. No deaths resulted in the stock rabbits in the same environment, fed on the same grain but with green grass in addition. Also, ten grams of skim-milk powder per rabbit per day prevented the death of the test rabbits as the extended heat wave permitted the demonstration. Similarly red clover hay, a replacement of the timothy, demonstrated that it also provided the protein needs to prevent deaths of the rabbits by the heat. According to the bioassays, the timothy suggests its own classification as of low potential as animal nutrition, even under extensive soil treatments growing it.

CHAPTER 13

Root Rot of Sweet Clover Reduced by Soil Fertility

ROOT ROT WAS PREVALENT in Missouri on numerous fields of second-year sweet clover during the cool, wet springs of 1946 and 1947. This "disease" was also observed on some of the sweet clover plots under fertility control in the four-year rotation of corn, oats, wheat, and sweet clover on the South Farm of the Missouri Experiment Station. Other adjacent plots on the Farm made normal growth and were apparently not infected.

Various investigators have reported that different plants growing on potassium-deficient soils are distinctly susceptible to root rot. Ginsburg reported that soybeans suffering a potash deficiency develop very few lateral roots and those are only near the root base. These roots decay easily. According to Eckstein, Bruno, and Turrentine potassium deficiency has a greater influence on the root development of biennial and perennial plants than on annuals.

Close observations were made in 1947 of the sweet clover on the plots at the Missouri Agricultural Experiment Station in order to ascertain whether there was any correlation between the levels of the soil fertility and the susceptibility of the sweet clover to this condition often spoken of as the "disease" of root rot. An attempt was also made to determine the effects of the "disease" on the growth of the plant and on the production of nitrogen within the crop.

The plots on the South Farm of the University of Missouri where the sweet clover was studied have been in the above rotation since 1938. The soil is a Putnam silt loam, typical of the clay-pan soils of Northeast Missouri where the "disease" was reported most prevalent.

Previous Soil Treatments Represented

A highly pure calcium carbonate limestone of ten-mesh, mill-run fineness had been applied to all plots at the rate of two tons per acre. On other plots additional treatments of phosphate alone or this in combination with potash had been made. The plots and the soil treatments used in these more careful observations and study were as follows:

Plot I—Limestone—2 tons each eight years.

Plot II—Limestone—2 tons each eight years plus 425 pounds of 20 per cent superphosphate in each rotation.

Plot III—Limestone—2 tons each eight years plus 425 pounds of 0-20-20 in each rotation.

The phosphate and the phosphate with the potash were applied as follows: 150 pounds in the row with the corn; 150 pounds drilled with the wheat, and 125 pounds drilled with oats. All crop residues were left on the land.

It was easily observed that the sweet clover on the plots receiving only limestone was badly infested with root rot. Only the roots near the surface of the soil were alive. The others were dead and had partially or even fully decomposed. The plants growing on the plots which received both limestone and superphosphate were more deeply rooted. They had much more top growth than those growing on the plots receiving limestone alone. Those growing on the plot receiving lime and both phosphate and potash had more root growth and much more top growth. The differences in weights of plant parts, in nitrogen content, and in the root rot are shown in Table 1. The plants growing where only limestone was used could be pulled up by hand. The plants growing on the other plots were deeply rooted and could only be removed with the help of a tile spade.

Yields and Nitrogen Content

Fractional samples of both roots and tops were harvested when in full bloom, air-dried, weighed, and the nitrogen content determined. These data are included with Table 1.

Discussion

The yield of air-dry roots harvested from the plots receiving limestone and phosphate exceeded that where limestone alone was used by 1,356 pounds or 65.5 per cent. Where both phosphate and potash were used along with the limestone, the harvest of roots exceeded that from where limestone alone was used by 1,572 pounds or over 75.8 per cent. Where limestone and phosphate were used, the yield of air-dry tops exceeded that where limestone alone was used by 2,730 pounds or 95.3 per cent. Where limestone, phosphate, and potash were used, the yield of air-dry tops exceeded that over limestone alone by 4,706 pounds or 164.3 per cent. In total growth of roots and tops where limestone and phosphate were both used, the yield of air-dry material was 4,086 more pounds or 83.3 per cent higher than where limestone alone was used. The yield of roots and tops where limestone, phosphate, and potash were used was 6,278 more pounds or 127.3 per cent higher than where limestone alone was used.

The total nitrogen in the tops and roots combined increased over 100 per cent as a result of the addition of phosphate and about 200 per cent as a consequence of the addition of both phosphate and potash.

The root rot infection varied from severe where limestone was used, to moderate where limestone and phosphate were used, to slight where limestone, phosphate, and potash were used.

Table 1

Hay Yields, Total Nitrogen, and Root Rot of Sweet Clover as Affected by Soil Treatments

Treatments	Pounds Per Acre				Root Rot
	Roots	Tops	Total Plant	Nitrogen	
Limestone..........................	2,072	2,864	4,936	80.0	Severe
Lime & Phosphate..............	3,428	5,594	9,022	162.0	Moderate
Increase over Limestone......	1,356	2,730	4,086	82.0	—
Lime, Phosphate & Potash...	3,644	7,570	11,214	240.4	Slight
Increase over Limestone......	1,572	4,706	6,278	160.4	—

Conclusions

The increased growth of roots and tops, and the larger amount of total nitrogen produced on the plots that received lime plus phosphate, and lime plus phosphate and potash, indicate that the additions to the soil of these inorganic plant nutrients reduced the susceptibility of the sweet clover to the root rot "disease".

These facts raise the question whether the root rot is a primary matter or whether it is one secondary to the deficiency of plant nutrients. There is the strong suggestion from these observations that the trouble of such a weakened root system is merely a consequence of the insufficient fertility and a condition to be remedied, not by an attempt to exterminate the micro-organism attacking the roots, but by feeding the plant more potash in a more fertile soil by which the plant roots are made non-susceptible to the root rot. Are we not about ready to say that the increasing incidence of what we call "disease" is the result of the decreasing fertility supply in our soils?

CHAPTER 14

Hidden Hunger
& Soil Fertility

HUNGER IS NOT a new problem. Next to the sex instinct, it is the principal force driving man and beast into action. It projects one into areas where he had not previously ventured either in body or in mind.

Today we understand hunger as world-wide in extent and importance. We are examining deeply enough into it to distinguish its "hidden" forms. We recognize these as due to shortages, not so much in the bulk of the food as in its nutritional qualities. We have not yet been able to tag all the different organic and inorganic compounds that provide these qualities, but have come to believe that many are *grown into* our foods. Consequently, we are thinking about deficiencies in the fertility of the soil as responsible for the failure of food to fully satisfy our body needs.

Hidden hungers are not experienced by man only. Even the microbes, the lowest forms of life, within the soil have their hidden hungers. Organic matter of the soil, which is the source of their energy food, accumulates in some deficient or acid soils while the microbes literally starve. In the face of abundance, hidden hungers exist for nitrogen, calcium and other elements of soil fertility. Under such conditions there is a surplus of bulk and a shortage of protein and growth-promoting compounds.

Sweet clover, fed as a green manure to the soil bacteria may cause hidden hunger for potassium. While this popular soil-improving legume grows and feeds ravenously on calcium, it can make bulk despite meagre supplies of potassium. It grows well enough on a pile of crushed limestone suitable for fertilizer use. But, it has manufactured little potassium into itself to satisfy the microbes. Thus the corn crop, which is expected to benefit from this green manure as a supplier of nitrogen actually is robbed by it of potassium in the process. In such cases, the soil microbes, too, are struggling to cover their hidden hunger.

Mature sweet clover residues of late summer, and straw left after the combine, plowed under before seeding a wheat crop, represent hidden hungers of microbes for nitrogen. The wheat crop also suffers but its hunger is not hidden. However, we do not appreciate the fact that the wheat crop "eats at the second table" and that the microbes in their hunger for nitrogen are literally passing this hunger on to the wheat crop.

Corn shows the same nitrogen hunger but this is usually interpreted as excessive thirst rather than lack of nitrogen. Thus the weather, over which we have no control, is made the scapegoat while we do nothing about the deficiency in the soil. It is important to note that both the corn and the microbes have plenty of energy food. Both, however, suffer from hidden hunger for small amounts of nitrogen by which their surplus energy foods can be converted into proteins and their diets balanced.

Even the lower forms of green plants, like the plankton in our fish ponds, suffer hidden hunger. In turn, the fish with their hunger for "grow foods" in more and better plankton do not multiply or grow so rapidly as when the fish ponds have proper food supplies.

Wild animals well up in the biological scale have their hidden hungers, too, though the fact is not always associated with the fertility of the soil. Animals that are strictly grass-eaters are not commonly found on the highly leached soils of the tropics. Instead buffaloes, elephants, antelopes and others of like species are found on the prairies and savannas. They subsist on mineral-rich soils, where natural legumes abound, which under cultivation produce hard, high-protein wheat.

The roaming of wild animals and their ravaging of farm crops usually indicates an effort to satisfy hidden hungers. In leaving the forest to graze on fertilized land, the deer signals his recognition of better nutritive values in the feed growing there. When cattle break through fences to get at the virgin soil of the highway or railroad right of way they reveal their instinct for nutritive food.

An animal's ability to detect differences in soil fertility—almost beyond our means of chemical detection, is not based on minerals. The animal is not looking to plants as haulers of minerals but as synthesizers of organic and organo-mineral complexes that build the animal body and supply energy. We have catalogued some of these complexes, but can we doubt that many yet remain unlisted? Much more is unknown than known about the nature and function of food factors, and the main provokers of hidden hunger may yet be unknown.

How shall we combat hidden hunger? Fortunately, we are better able to combat these hungers at the point of origin, that is in the soil, than at any later stage. Prevention is simpler than cure. At that point the problem is no more complex perhaps than supplying one or more inorganic elements. Cure the hidden hunger of microbes and plants and you prevent the hidden hunger of animals and humans. The further removed from the soil the more nearly insurmountable the problem of supplying the diet with essential minerals, vitamins, amino acids, etc.

Lespedeza hay grown after phosphate application and fed to sheep caused them to grow fleeces that were low in fat or yolk and that scoured out too poorly to be carded except as broken fibers. Yet the same kind of hay grown on soil treated with both lime and phosphate helped grow fleeces of heavy yolk and wool that scoured well and carded out as fibers of good quality. Treating the soil was simple; but to figure out what supplement to feed the sheep to make better wool is not so simple. Cure is extremely perplexing but prevention is as simple as, in this case, liming the soil.

In our thinking about "diseases" both empirical and scientific knowledge are influencing us to think less about cure and more about prevention by ministering to sick soils. Once the mind thinks in terms of soil fertility, observations come rapidly. Calves eating plaster, not the exposed first coat but the hidden last coat in a fine barn, prompted a farmer to ferret out a magnesium deficiency in his soils. Prompted by curiosity and intelligence to use some magnesium as a fertilizer he started a train of apparent miracles, including the curing of scours in calves, and some reduced mortality, less mastitis in the cows, better alfalfa, better corn, and other blessings on his farm.

When other major and minor mineral elements given to cattle make them negative to the blood test for brucellosis; and when medical research is pointing to similar suggestions for improvement of undulant fever patients, these are no longer hidden troubles. Attention to the soil as the point of origin of diseases as deficiencies, as major hungers, calls for major attention by more of us than those of the curative professions alone.

It can be truthfully said that rapid progress is being made in recognizing hidden hungers. Many of them are now being prevented because they are being diagnosed as originating in our declining soil fertility. Foremost among the gross decline is the loss of protein synthesis by plants. Soil treatments are no longer desirable only because they produce more bulk per acre. They are applied to increasing acres also because they add to the nutritional quality of the crops, which relieve a long chain of hidden hungers coming up from the soil through the entire biotic pyramid to torment man at the top. For better reproduction of farm animals, and for the better health for them and for ourselves as well, we are becoming increasingly concerned to know more about soil fertility as the guarantee of good fortune.

The disturbing hidden hungers are hidden mainly from our thought, our recognition, and our full appreciation of their origin. They are not hidden from our physiology, nor from our mental processes, when as little iodine as a fraction of a grain coming up from our soils through plants is all that "stands between us and imbecility".

It is a good sign for the future that we are coming to realize that our hidden hungers are provoking deficiencies in mind as well as body. We are coming to think about keeping up the soil in order to keep us mentally able to realize that our hidden hungers are pointing to the soil fertility as ready means for their prevention.

CHAPTER 15

Soil Fertility
& the Quality of Seeds

THE INFLUENCE OF SOIL fertility on the quantitative aspects of plant growth is well known since the production of dry matter by plants is the criterion by which soil fertility is usually assessed. However, measurements of yield alone (as weight or volume) leave something to be desired, when yield alone does not necessarily indicate the ability of the plant to perform the reproductive and other functions for which it was intended. Soil fertility is now recognized as a factor influencing such diverse properties as the quality of forage and seed crops, and the milling and baking qualities of grains. Up to this moment, little attention has been given to the possible modification of seed germination and seedling development that results according to the level of nutrition which was a part of the environment of the parent plant.

The seeding of crops, one of the major items of labor and expense for a farmer, is often a failure. Often no satisfactory reasons for seeding failures are available. It is interesting to postulate that the causes of many such failures, especially those attributed to "damping off," may be traceable to seeds which, although normal in appearance, may be so deficient in some "vital" quality as to render them incapable of producing vigorous seedlings.

The hypothesis proposed for test is stated in three parts:

1. Soil fertility has an influence upon the elemental composition of seed.
2. The chemical and biochemical composition of the seed influences the cellular metabolism of the germinating embryo.
3. The metabolic activity of the seed and the nutrients available to the germinating embryo are factors in the germination of the seed and in the seedling vigor.

Experimental Methods

To test the proposed hypothesis, some seeds of wheat grown in field plots under various specific levels of soil fertility were subjected to tests of germination and seedling vigor. Determinations were made of the compositions and weights of seeds and embryos. The activities of two enzyme systems and properties related to respiration were estimated.

Wheat was grown in field plots at locations in central and southeastern Nebraska and in central and southeastern Missouri. Soil treatments differed at the various locations according to the potentials of plant nutrition there. In central Nebraska, nitrogen was the fertilizer element used. In southeastern Nebraska, nitrogen and phosphorus were used; at the Missouri locations, soil treatments included, in addition, calcium, magnesium, sulfur, potassium and trace elements.

Seedling vigor, or the "germinating power" of Nadvornik, was determined by planting seeds in sterile quartz sand. The depth of planting was three inches for the initial studies, but in later work this was reduced to two inches. After incubation in a constant temperature (20° C.) chamber, the numbers of plants which had emerged at various time intervals were determined. The moisture content of the sand was supplied according to the formula given in USDA Handbook No. 30.

An "index of seedling vigor" was devised to aid in the presentation of bulky data. This value was calculated by dividing the sum of the seedlings visible at each time of counting by the number of seedlings which were visible at the final count, and multiplying by 100. High values for the "index of seedling vigor" indicate early emergence.

Two estimates of respiration were obtained. Oxygen utilization was determined by means of the Warburg apparatus, and an estimate of carbohydrate respiration was made by a simple test devised for these experiments. The oven dry weight of seeds, before and after germination, was determined and the loss in weight of the seeds was taken as an indication of respiration.

Phosphatase activity was determined in homogenates of wheat sprouts which had been grown under standard conditions. The method followed was essentially that used by Sommer. Phytase activity was estimated by the amount of phosphoric acid liberated when seeds were germinated for various periods of time. The method of Fontaine *et al.* was used with slight modifications.

Wheat embryos were excised for chemical analysis, using the method described by Brown and Morris.

Results & Discussion

Studies of seed quality indicate that seedling development is influenced by the nutritive environment by which the parent plant of the seed was grown. It is not possible to predict the nature of the seedling's response from a knowledge of only the nutrients applied through a fertilizer. The level of nutrition contributed by the soil and climatic conditions under which the seed was grown are also important factors for consideration. Likewise, balanced nutrition of the parent plant was indicated as being an important factor in determining the seed's quality.

Germination & Seedling Vigor

Nitrogen: Preliminary studies of seedling vigor using paired samples of high nitrogen and low nitrogen wheat grown in central and southeastern Nebraska indicated that emergence of seedlings was improved when the nitrogen of the grain was increased. Nine paired samples were used in this study. A summary of data from these experiments is given in Table 1.

In these tests the samples of wheat having the highest crude protein contents were outstanding because of the green color and vigor of the seedlings. Subsequent experiments using wheat grown at North Platte, Nebraska, under unfavorable moisture conditions (dry, not winds) indicated that varying levels of nitrogen moved into the grain from urea spray affected seedling emergence adversely (Figure 1). This effect was not evident when the nitrogen content of the seed was increased through applications of ammonium nitrate to the soil (Figure 2).

Table 1

Emergence of Wheat Seedlings According to the Crude Protein of the Wheat Grain Used as Seed. (Data Given as Percent)

Crude Protein		Emergence*		
		6 days	10 days	21 days
High protein wheat	14.4	15.6	92.0	91.0
Low protein wheat	11.0	10.7	85.3	85.7
Difference	3.4	4.9	6.7**	5.3

*Emergence through three inches of quartz sand.
**Just significant at 5% level t = 2.389.

Wheat from nitrogen fertilized plots gave improved seedling emergence at two locations in eastern Missouri.

Phosphorus: An important role for phosphorus was indicated by the effect of this element as a fertilizer on the emergence of wheat seedlings. When this nutrient was deficient in the soil, the use of moderate amounts of phosphorus in the fertilizer generally improved seed quality as measured by seedling emergence. Higher rates of phosphorus often decreased emergence. This effect was noted especially in wheat seed produced in southeastern Nebraska (Figure 3) and the phosphorus deficient Oliver silt loam soil of southeastern Missouri. The starter fertilizer used on the Oliver soil had the formula 8-24-8.

An "index of seedling vigor" can be used to advantage for expressing the rate at which seedlings emerge. The results are tabulated for one experiment using seed produced in southeastern Nebraska in Table 2. From the data in this table, two trends can be noted: (1) nitrogen which moved into the grain late decreased the index of seedling vigor; (2) but at this particular rate of nitrogen fertilizer, the phosphorus fertilization increased the index of seedling vigor, i.e. seedlings emerged through 2 inches of sand in a shorter time.

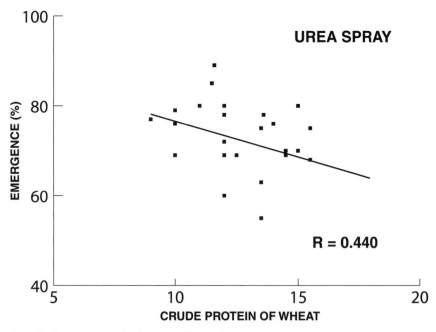

Fig. 1—Emergence of wheat seedlings from grains of various protein contents. Nitrogen applied as urea spray.

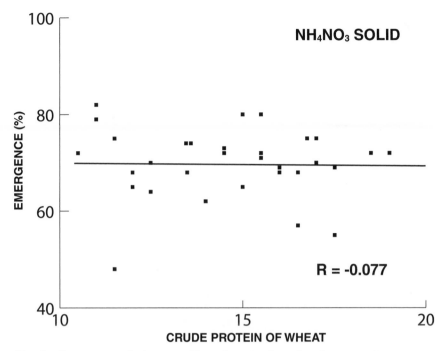

Fig. 2—Emergence of wheat seedlings from grains of various protein contents. Nitrogen fertilizer applied as ammonium nitrate.

Composition of Wheat Grain & Embryo

The germinating embryos and the developing seedlings are dependent upon the seed for mineral nutrients and energy material. The seed's chemical composition gives an indication of the total mineral nutrients available for utilization during germination. A measure of the energy material can be obtained from the seed weight since the reserves of the endosperm constitute most of the weight of the wheat grain.

In addition to its function as a storehouse for nutrient materials, the endosperm contains much of the enzyme machinery for endosperm digestion. The embryo also contains enzymes for resynthesis, into cellular components, of the products of endosperm digestion. The enzymes are:

Nitrogen fertilization has a pronounced effect on the phosphorus content of both the whole grain and the embryo (Figures 6, 7). Davidson noted this effect. He explained it as a stimulating effect of nitrogen fertilizer on growth. In contrast to the nitrogen composition, the phosphorus content of the embryo varied more than that of the endosperm. These facts are interesting since they demonstrate that, at least in some respects, the seed

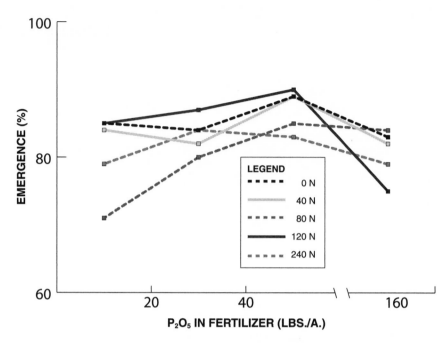

Fig. 3—Emergence of wheat seedlings through 2 inches of sand after 10 days according to the rate of nitrogen and phosphorus fertilization of the parent plants. Bennet, Nebraska samples.

Table 2

Seedling Vigor as Influenced by the Rate of Phosphorus Fertilization and the Date of Nitrogen Fertilization of the Parent Plant. Samples from Bennet, Nebraska.

P_2O_5 Applied (Lb./Acre)	Date of Nitrogen Application				
	Oct. 8	Apr. 25	May 7	May 24	Mean
0	4.52#	5.31	5.39	4.77	5.00
20	5.11	5.27	5.10	4.69	5.02
40	5.17	5.25	5.19	4.69	5.06
160	5.25	5.45	5.39	4.89	5.24
Avg.	5.01	5.32	5.25	4.76	

#Seedlings visible at date of counting their emergence as percent of the total number finally emerged.

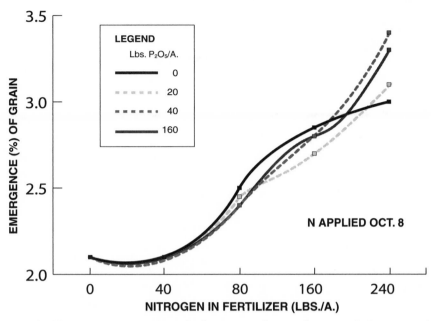

Fig. 4—Nitrogen concentration of wheat according to the rate of nitrogen and phosphorus fertilization. Bennet, Nebraska.

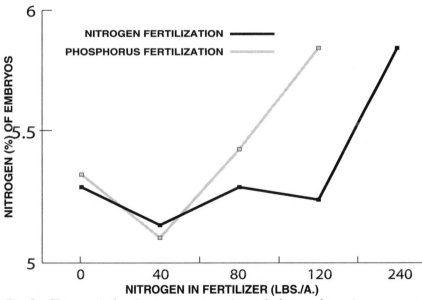

Fig. 5—Changes in the nitrogen concentrations of wheat embryos in response to nitrogen and phosphorus fertilization. Values are averages of all phosphorus or nitrogen levels.

is subject to considerable variation; and that variations within the embryo may exceed those within the storage tissue.

Phosphorus: Phosphorus fertilization had only small effect on the chemical composition of the seed or the embryo. This indicates that the effect of phosphorus fertilizers on seedling vigor may be an indirect one.

Weight of Seeds

Weights of the seeds and the embryos were influenced by nitrogen fertilization in a manner which was unrelated to the yield of the seed grain. High nitrogen treatments, which were usually quite ineffective in providing increased yields, consistently produced smaller seed than did the lower rates of nitrogen. Fertilizer treatments which increased the yield of grain did not necessarily give seed which weighed less. Thus, the higher nitrogen contents of the nitrogen-fertilized seed and the embryos were off-set, in part, by the small size of these seeds and embryos. These relationships are presented in Figures 8 and 9. High nitrogen content, low phosphorus

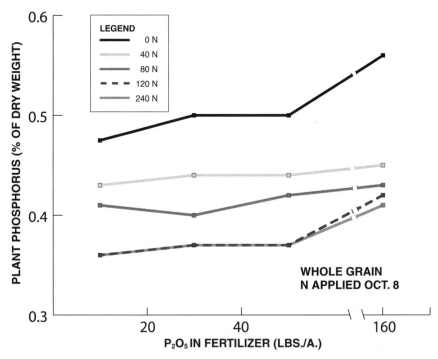

Fig. 6—Phosphorus concentration of wheat according to the rate of nitrogen and phosphorus fertilization. Bennet, Nebraska.

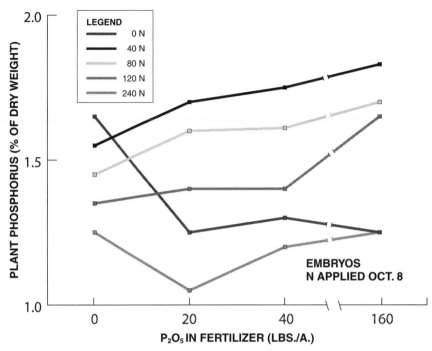

Fig. 7—Phosphorus concentration of wheat embryos according to the rate of nitrogen and phosphorus fertilization. Bennet, Nebraska.

content and small seeds were related to high levels of nitrogen fertilization. Low phosphorus and small seed were additive in their depressing effects on the total phosphorus content of high-nitrogen seed. The addition of one nutrient in large quantities may adversely affect the level of another, thus upsetting the balance which is considered necessary for normal function of metabolic processes.

The early work at Nebraska by Lyon and then later by Kiesselbach indicated that the weight of wheat kernels may influence the final yield of wheat. Kiesselbach reviewed the literature on this subject and found substantial agreement with the results he had obtained.

Phosphatase Activity

Measures of the release of inorganic phosphorus during germination, presumably by the action of phytase on phytin, indicated that this function is influenced slightly by seed composition. Treatments which increased yields and decreased phosphorus of the seed gave low values for phytase

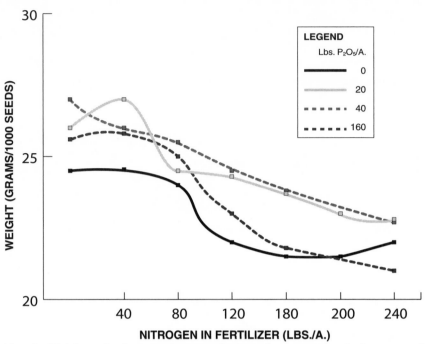

Fig. 8—Weights of wheat grain according to the amounts of nitrogen and phosphorus applied as fertilizer. Bennet, Nebraska.

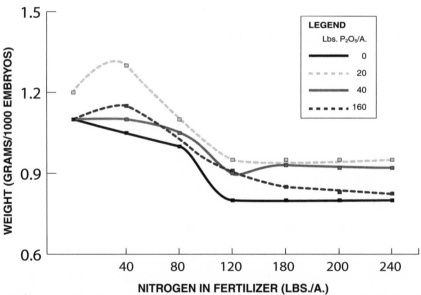

Fig. 9—Weights of excised embryos from wheat grain according to the rate of nitrogen and phosphorus fertilization. Bennet, Nebraska.

activity. There was a close relationship between the amount of nitrogen fertilizer applied to the wheat plant and the inorganic phosphorus content of the ungerminated grain (Figure 10). Here is an indication that improved nitrogen nutrition increased the ability of the plant to synthesize organic phosphorus compounds at the expense of inorganic phosphorus.

Phosphatase activity of wheat samples from Bennet, Nebraska was increased by increasing the amount of nitrogen in the fertilizer (Figure 11). The nitrogen which reached the grain via the soil from spring (April 25) applications of nitrogen was apparently more effectively converted to phosphatase than was the nitrogen applied in the fall. Nitrogen applied on the soil on May 7 was less effective in this respect than was that applied on April 25. Evidence is presented in Figure 12 that nitrogen which was moved into the grain as a result of spraying with urea at heading time was effectively converted into the enzyme. These results are in agreement with those of Valy and Pokary who studied the effect of nitrogen nutrition on

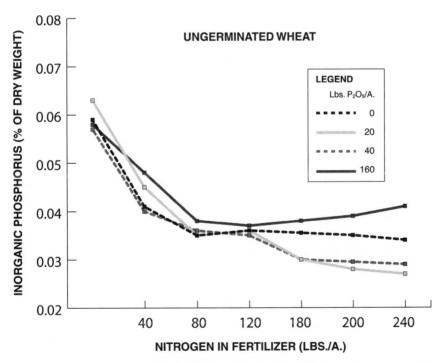

Fig. 10—*Inorganic phosphorus concentration of ungerminated wheat grain according to the rate of nitrogen and phosphorus fertilization. Bennet, Nebraska.*

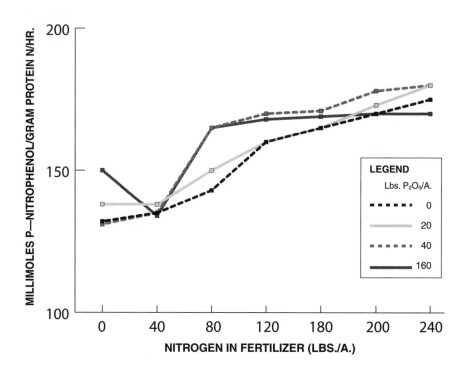

Fig. 11—Phosphatase activity of a preparation of ground wheat sprouts as influenced by the rates of nitrogen and phosphorus fertilizations of the parent plants.

the catalase of the wheat plant, and with the work done by Virtanen with bacteria. Virtanen has summarized the work of his laboratory by stating:

"...the enzymatic activity of cells depends decisively on their nitrogen content and that we have possibilities of producing low nitrogen cells enzymatically very different from normal cells. The observations made with bacteria show conclusively the decisive significance of nitrogen nutrition to the cell metabolism. Also from the point of nutrition of higher plants and animals the above results are in my opinion interesting as it can be assumed that in their cells, too, a great quantitative and qualitative deficiency of N-nutrition brings about similar changes in the enzymatic machinery of cells as in micro-organisms.

Wheat from locations in southeastern Missouri gave phosphatase activities which differed according to the treatments on the various soils (Table 3). Samples which were grown without nitrogen fertilizers were among the lowest in enzyme activity. The highest activity was associated with high fertilizer treatments.

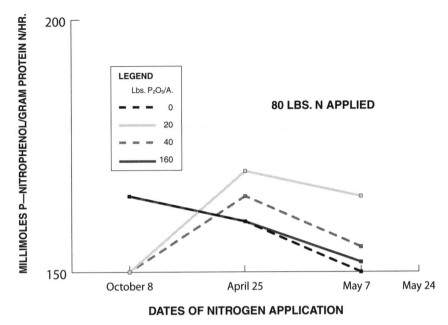

Fig. 12—Phosphatase activity of a preparation of ground wheat sprouts as influenced by the rate of phosphorus fertilization and date of nitrogen fertilization of the parent plants (as determined by the method using para-nitrophenol phosphate).

Respiration

Results from studies of respiration were largely inconclusive. High-nitrogen seed utilized slightly less oxygen on a per-seed basis than did low nitrogen seed; but oxygen utilization was greatest for this treatment when results were expressed in terms of weight. The high-phosphorus treatment gave a slightly higher value for oxygen utilization than did other phosphorus treatments. These results presented in Table 4, seem to indicate that seed composition has little influence on the enzyme systems which are involved in the respiration of energy materials.

Summary

Wheat was harvested from plants which were grown with varying levels of applied nutrients on soils which represented a range in degree of soil development according to the intensity of climatic forces. Seeds were tested for their ability to germinate and for the vigor of their seedlings. Certain attributes were measured which may influence seedling performance.

Table 3

Phosphatase Activity of a Preparation of Ground Wheat Sprouts as Influenced by the Fertilizer Treatments by which the Wheat Grain was Grown. Samples from Three Soils of Southeast Missouri. Values Expressed are Millimoles P-Nitrophenol Per Gram Protein-Nitrogen Per Hour at 37.5° C.

Fertilizer Treatment	Oliver	Menfro	Yazoo
None	158	151	170
33-0-0	168	168	182
66-0-0	178	162	174
33-0-0 + starter	158	171	189
66-0-0 + starter	173	178	176
100-0-0 + starter	167	188	178
132-0-0 + starter	178		208
132-300-0 + starter	152		204
132-300-200 + starter	170		200
132-300-200 + starter + MgS	171		224
132-300-200 + starter + MgS + Trace	182		197

Seedling vigor was influenced by the fertilizer supplied to the parent plant. There was evidence that climatic factors modified the effect of nitrogen fertilization. During a favorable year, seedling emergence was improved when the nitrogen content of the seed increased. This effect was not evident, or was even reversed, during an unfavorable year. Moderate amounts of phosphorus improved seedling emergence but large quantities of this nutrient depressed it. There was evidence that fertilization for high yields may not give seeds which are highest in quality. Seed which came from plants fertilized with large quantities of major nutrients, and trace elements in addition, often were among the lowest in giving vigorous seedlings. The importance of balanced nutrition was indicated.

The added nutrients had an important influence on the composition of both the whole seed and the embryo. Nitrogen fertilization increased the nitrogen content and decreased the phosphorus content of both seed and embryo.

The higher rates of nitrogen fertilization decreased the size of both seed and embryo.

Table 4

Oxygen Utilization and Loss of Energy Material by Germinating Wheat Seed.
(Samples from Nitrogen-Phosphorus Interaction Experiment, Bennet, Nebraska)

Fertilizer Treatment P$_2$O$_5$ (Lbs./Acre)	Oxygen Utilized		Loss of Carbohydrates after 5 days (% of original weight)
	ml/hr/10 seed	Ml/hr/gm	
0	73.3	267.5	12.6
20	66.4	234.6	11.4
40	74.9	268.4	11.8
160	75.9	273.0	11.8
N (Lbs./Acre)			
0	76.1	264.2	11.6
40	78.4	260.5	12.5
80	71.1	255.7	11.3
120	69.9	255.1	12.5
240	67.7	270.8	11.6

Phosphatase activity per unit of protein-nitrogen was increased by nitrogen fertilization, while less inorganic phosphorus was liberated from the seed of higher nitrogen content.

Two measures of respiration failed to indicate any important, consistent change in this process by either the nitrogen or phosphorus content of the seed.

These results indicate that certain properties of the seed and seedling performance are changed by the level of nutrition by which the seeds were grown.

CHAPTER 16

Quality as Feed, Not Only Quality as Crop, Demonstrates Effects of Soil Fertility

CROP YIELDS HAVE LONG been measured by the amount of the plant mass. If crops are grown for the simple purpose of selling them, and if we measure the returns by the greatest monetary income from more pounds or bushels sold, then bigger plants may be the reason for making soils more fertile. In a broader sense, it is the fertile soils that make the plants grow bigger. Though there may be big plants of some kind that grow big on soils that are not very fertile for other plants, one cannot conclude, therefore, that any big vegetative mass proves the soil to be fertile. One can reason the converse of this quite safely, however, and say small, spindly, sick plants are indicators of an infertile soil."

Certain "big" plants are more apt to be indicators of fertile soils than others. But for that, one must know something about what the plant is creating or making while it is growing. Crops, like the legumes, which are said to be "hard to grow," are usually indicators of fertile soils when they are making big plants and especially a big output of seed. It is this reproductive aspect, the activity of making new cells, of creating proteins—through which alone life keeps flowing—and of multiplying its parts and its species that really reports the fertile soils. Plants in Nature are big and numerous because they have been multiplying themselves via production of more protein. The production of protein by plants is the real index of the fertility of the soil under the plants.

Perhaps you have never thought that what we consider plant growth is not necessarily multiplication of cells, for which more protein must be created by the biosynthetic, or life, processes of the plant. Instead, it may be only a case of blowing up to larger volume the cells laid down in embryonic age. It may be making bigger those cells by putting in more water or more sugar and other carbohydrates of photosynthetic origin. In the watermelon, and other cucurbits, this is the case. So the so-called "growth" reflects mainly the air, water, and sunshine going into the resulting products of sugar equivalent and not the fertility coming up from the soil to convert those carbohydrates into proteins, as we expect it to be done by legumes.

But when the plant's embryo is the place where the cells are all laid down, even in very miniature, then the truly growth process there calls for much soil fertility and that in balanced proportions of the different nutrient elements. Even a watermelon requires a fertile soil in a certain sense, but we are apt to be misled in believing that the increasing size of the plant or the increasing amounts of plant product are necessarily proof of fertile soils. That fact has been demonstrated for soybean plants readily by shifting the fertility ratio, or the balance between calcium and potassium. We associate the function of the latter with the plant's production of vegetative mass; the former is connected with the output of protein by the biosynthetic conversion of the photosynthetic products or carbohydrates into protein. Thus by unbalanced soil fertility we may be misled to believe that big plants mean big soil. But with balanced fertility, we are correct and fertile soils really mean big plants in terms of much protein.

There is no fallacious reasoning in saying that less fertile soils give us the small, sick plants, when on other soils along side the plants are large. In the same field one can demonstrate this fact easily. Applications of the elements deficient in the soil soon show their effects in terms of bigger plants. Nitrogen on grasses in the pasture as a result of urine droppings is a well known example in the spots of tall-growing plants. Lime on legumes like the sweet clover and alfalfa, magnesium on soybeans, zinc on fruit trees, copper on clovers in Australia and numerous other soil treatments draw their lines of differences clearly out in the field.

The sickly conditions of the plants give various signs and symptoms. Celery with its dark areas in the stalk when boron is insufficient; white-colored soybean leaves except for green veins when magnesium is deficient in the soil, reddening leaves of cotton under potassium deficiency, clustered small leaves in rosette-like forms of fruit trees needing more zinc from the soil or from spray applications, are all telling us that infertile soils make not only small but also sick plants.

We are gradually coming to realize that plant growth is a creative activity by a life form demanding proper nourishment if that growth is to go forward effectively. Bigger plants generally testify to a fertile soil, especially if bigger yields of seed and more extensive cell reproduction rather than just cell enlargement are the reasons for bigness. Conversely, small sickly plants are true indicators of poor nutrition of them by the soil. Closer observation of our plants and more knowledge of the symptoms of plant hunger are bringing us around to feed our plants via the soil rather than turn them out to rustle for themselves. On fertile soils alone can our crops be truly big in the food-creating services we expect of them.

CHAPTER 17

White Clover Years
in Cycles of Soil Changes

WHY WE DON'T have a good crop of white clover and the fine honey from it every year, or why this kind of clover comes seemingly in cycles of about the biblical seven years, are not new queries. The beliefs they imply have been more than just fancy in the minds of older observers of the volunteer white clover coming into the bluegrass pastures and lawns in periodic years. The inquirers have connected the intermittent appearance of white clover with certain kinds of soils. They have emphasized this cycle of dominance by this kind of clover especially on the glaciated, the windblown, and on the other more fertile soils where the growths of the bluegrass are also good. Some have believed that the "white clover year" is the "normal" one after a year or two of drought.

That we may expect white clover prominence in cycles of years is the suggestion from some soils studies in Missouri. Those studies suggest that this crop's periodic prevalence is related to the increasing degree of the soil's saturation by exchangeable calcium which favors the nutrition, and thereby the appearance and growth, of such a legume. So, theoretically then, we may well look to cycles of increase and depletion of exchangeable calcium as possibly the cause of the white clover cycles. We may well expect this where the soil contains a reserve of weatherable calcium-bearing minerals in the surface or subsoil, as the glacier, for example, might have left it. Also, it would seem reasonable where un-weathered floodplain deposits of silt, brought in from the arid West by the Missouri River for example, are constantly blowing from there and renewing the surface soil by these calcareous deposits on the soils of north Missouri. Then, too, when the clay of the soil, resulting from the weathering of the original minerals, is a partially reversible colloid which adsorbs the active fertility elements while moist (but may not take them up again when wetted after it lost them through severe drying), the very prominent white clover of the 1956 spring makes us give consideration to the suggestive data from some soil studies under continuous bluegrass sod.

Based on Soil Samples

Apropos of the belief that the "white clover year" is a sequel to one of drought, the studies included soil samples collected annually from 1931 to 1938 inclusive, the last of which was considered a "white clover year." The plots went out of cultivation and into the blue grass sod in 1930. While the 50-year average of the annual rainfall was 34.44 inches at Bethany, Missouri, the site of the Soil Conservation Research Station where the soils were studied, it was but 24.43 and 21.80 inches for the two years, 1936 and 1937 respectively, preceding the clover prominence. The former of these is well remembered for its disastrous heat and drought during June, July, and August. Also in 1934, there had been an almost equally serious drought. During the first half of the year 1938, the total rainfall was 16.06 inches with the amounts of 2.50, 4.39, and 3.07 inches for the months of April, May, and June respectively, to invite the white clover in what would seem nearly normal precipitation.

Starting with 1931, the soil samples were taken annually in a series of plots. But particular study was made of the changes in the soil under continuous bluegrass sod. This was given no soil treatment. It had no crops removed and was showing no more erosion than what would amount to carrying the surface seven inches of soil away in 4,545 years. The soil changes suggest themselves as theoretical reasons for the cycles of periodic prominence of white clover in continuous bluegrass. They suggest corresponding cycles of fluctuating growths in the sod crop too. These would go unnoticed since they do not call themselves to our attention by such flash of color as does the white clover.

The soil under sod was examined carefully by one-inch layers in order to measure the changes with time more accurately. This plot served as the basis for measuring the changes in the other plots undergoing fertility treatments, and surface soil losses. It was the check for the rates at which the other plot profiles were being truncated or whittled off at their tops. The sod plot was "the standard" in the study.

Soil samples for the alternate years 1931, 1933, 1935, and 1937 were considered sufficient numbers to show the changes in the soil fertility. Since legumes like white clover require calcium (and magnesium) generously, it is significant to note the increase in the exchangeable calcium during those seven years before the one of white clover prominence. For these four odd-numbered years the percentages saturation by calcium of the soil's exchange capacity stepped up in the following order, 56.96, 55.09, 69.70, and 70.96, respectively. Since for better crops of legumes, like alfalfa, the experiences with soil tests correlated with the crops suggested that the calcium saturation should be brought up to 75%, it seems highly probable that this increase in the soil's saturation by this dibasic nutrient ion might be enough to invite white clover when at the lower figure the deficient calcium was prohibiting it.

When the saturations of the soil by calcium combined with magnesium were considered, the values fluctuated between a low of 75.45% and a high of 90.85% during those years. The high value represents a soil well stocked with these two essentials for protein-producing crops like white clover and other legumes in general. Thus, we might expect the white clover to come back because the fertility improved so much in respect to calcium. Since none was applied, the incidence of the white clover suggests that either the reserve soil minerals or those recently blown in were weathered enough during the absence of the clover to bring the active fertility up again to meet the needs of the clover in this respect.

The total exchange capacity of the soil remained constant during those years. The figures for the four samplings within the seven-year period were 19.98, 19.06, 19.20, and 19.35 milligram equivalents, respectively.

Of particular interest was the increase in the organic matter of the soil as a result of growing the bluegrass. As per cent of the dry soil, the figures for the four years cited were 3.53, 3.71, 4.07, and 4.29, respectively. The total nitrogen also increased according to the following per cents of the dry soil, 0.173, 0.185, 0.190, and 0.205, respectively.

One might have expected this increase in nitrogen to give it more activity in growing more bluegrass. But while this more stable organic matter of the soil was increasing, it was not becoming any the less woody or less carbonaceous to increase its rate of liberating its nitrogen, phosphorus, potassium, calcium, or any other of its nutrients. This was shown by the nearly constant carbon-nitrogen ratios of it. Those values during the four sampled years cited for the seven-year period were respectively 11.85, 11.63, 12.41, and 12.15. The organic matter seemed relatively too stable for any shift to speedy decomposition without tillage. Thus the bluegrass sod was building up the more permanent organic matter. It was increasing the percentages saturation of the soil with those inorganic essentials by which the white clover would be encouraged, since as a legume it needed little nitrogen from the soil and could build its own protein-rich organic matter from atmospheric nitrogen. This organic matter, dropped back to the soil on the death of the white clover, would provide extra and active nitrogen. It would invite subsequent lush growth of the bluegrass. This non-legume would compete with the next crop of clover for other fertility elements liberated because the added nitrogen would hasten the decomposition of the more carbonaceous soil organic matter to set them free or make them active again.

Thus we can visualize the bluegrass exhausting the soil's supply of active nitrogen and of other active fertility, and building these into more stable organic matter even with an increase in total nitrogen. This was happening while the decomposition of the reserve minerals was releasing extra calcium to saturate the soil's exchange capacity more highly with this active, essential cation. This would favor the advent and the growth of a legume crop, like white clover, which fixes atmospheric nitrogen. But this clover growth would reduce the calcium saturation to the hindrance of its own future growth. It would put extra and active nitrogen into the soil. So while eliminating itself by exhaustion of the active calcium, it would favor the bluegrass by providing the active nitrogen.

The time period required for building up the sufficiently increased calcium saturation needed for the white clover suggests itself as the time interval between the "white clover years." That interval may well include "drought" years for whatever changes in the soil or cycle they bring about. Such are the theoretical suggestions for the number of inter-clover years on soils of the Kansan glaciation given loess deposits and located in the climatic setting of north Missouri. They are presented to be confirmed or refuted by further studies of soil fertility in relation to the periodic annual growths of white clover in our permanent pastures and lawns.

CHAPTER 18

Why White Clover Years

WHY ISN'T THERE a heavy white clover growth every year? Why does a heavy crop of the showy legume seem to appear in seven-year cycles? These are some of the old questions brought to life following this spring's heavy white clover growth.

And these are logical questions and rot just a fancy in the minds of older observers who have noted that volunteer white clover comes into bluegrass pasture and lawns in periodic years.

Those who have noted the white clover cycle have different theories regarding its regular appearance. Some say it's connected with glaciated, windblown, and other fertile soils where bluegrass grows well. Others believe white clover years are normal ones following drouth years.

It's known that soils under sod gather increasing amounts of calcium through weathering processes over a period of years. This would supply a basis for better nutrition and, thereby to the appearance and growth, of legumes.

So, cycles of calcium increase and depletion may bring about white clover years. A soil under sod may spend a number of years building up its calcium reserve to the point where white clover can take advantage of the reserve and make a sudden growth. But, at the same time, this growth depletes the calcium reserve to the point where it will not be able to feed a second year's clover crop.

This may be especially true where soils have a reserve of weatherable calcium minerals in the surface or subsoil. These could be north Missouri River hill soils continually getting new deposits of unweathered soil from dry western areas or glaciated soils.

Also, it's known that clay, a result of weathering, is a partially reversible particle. That is, clay will absorb and hold fertility elements while moist but will lose its grip through severe drying and may not re-absorb the elements readily when wetted again. This would leave the fertility elements available to legumes following dry years.

In regard to the idea that white clover years follow one of drouth, looking at a study of soil samples collected at Bethany from 1931 through 1938, the final year of the study, 1938, was considered a white clover year.

Many Missourians remember 1936 for its disastrous heat and drouth. There had also been an almost equally serious drouth in 1934 and, in 1937, rainfall at Bethany amounted only to 22 inches as compared to the 50-year average of 35 inches at that location.

So, under near normal moisture conditions in the spring of 1938, white clover made one of its periodic heavy appearances. Conditions were similar to those of 1938 in parts of Missouri this spring. Previous years had been dry and white clover made another of its periodic appearances.

Going back to the seven-year soil study, samples were taken annually from a number of plots. One of the plots was in continuous bluegrass soil. It received no soil treatment, had no crops removed, and showed little erosion.

The sod plot was studied carefully to measure time changes accurately. This plot served as the basis for measuring changes in other plots undergoing fertility treatments, surface soil losses, and other processes. The sod plot was the "standard" in the study.

Soil changes during the study supply Albrecht's theory for white clover cycles in continuous bluegrass. The study also suggests similar cycles of greater bluegrass growth. However, bluegrass cycles aren't as noticeable as white clover cycles since the grass has no such flash of color as does white clover.

During the study period, calcium content of the soil's exchange capacity increased from 57 to 71 percent. Since other soil tests have shown that a soil's calcium level should be brought up to 75 percent for better legume crops, it seems highly probably that an increase in calcium content might be enough to invite sudden growth of white clover.

When an increasing magnesium content was considered along with the calcium, the exchange value varied from a low of 75.5 and a high of 91 percent during these years. The high figure represents a soil well-stocked with the two essentials for protein-producing legume crops.

Since no calcium or magnesium was applied, the arrival of white clover in 1938, suggests that either reserve soil minerals, or those recently blown in, were weathered enough to bring the active fertility up enough to meet the clover's needs.

Of particular interest was the soil's increase in organic matter and nitrogen as a result of growing bluegrass. Organic matter jumped from 3.5 percent of the dry soil to 4.3 percent during the seven years while nitrogen increased from .17 to .21 percent.

This nitrogen increase might be expected to give bluegrass sod a push. But, while the organic matter of the soil was increasing, it wasn't becoming any less woody. This prevented the soil from increasing its rate of decay or of freeing its nitrogen, phosphorus, potassium, calcium, or any other nutrient.

Thus, during the absence of white clover, the bluegrass sod was building up more permanent organic matter that would slow its growth. It was increasing inorganic soil essentials that encourage white clover since legumes need little nitrogen from the soil as they can build their own protein-rich organic matter from nitrogen in the air.

This protein-rich, highly decayable organic matter dropped back to the soil at the end of the white clover year. This provided extra and active nitrogen and hastened the decay of woody organic matter to set free and activate fertility elements. In turn, this invited lush bluegrass growth that competed with the clover crop.

So, the richer soils staying under sod are in a continual process. The sod builds up the soil's organic matter and accumulates minerals through the weathering process. Clover comes in at periodic intervals to take advantage of the weathered minerals, gives the organic matter the nitrogen needed to speed up decay which, in turn, boosts bluegrass growth.

The years needed to build up the calcium level to the point where it can be used by white clover suggests itself as the time interval between white clover years. This interval may well include drouth years for whatever changes in the soil or cycle they bring about.

Such are the theories about white clover years on the more fertile north Missouri soils. They are presented to be confirmed or disclaimed by further studies of soil fertility in relation to white clover growth.

CHAPTER 19

Diversity of Amino Acids in Legumes According to the Soil Fertility

AGRICULTURE IS CONCERNED with the synthesis of food. Our ultimate goal in this industry has always been the increase of production, *i.e.* greater numbers and more pounds, per acre. Too often only such physical attributes of the products—even of people—are of prime consideration when some other criteria are of more fundamental importance. We neglect the quality of our food products and continue to measure our output only in bushels and tons per acre.

In accordance with the long-held belief that a specific crop is of value because it produces much bulk, we have imported many exotic plants in the hope of maintaining a high level of food production. While watching the delivery of bulk, we have kept up the synthesis of caloric compounds by plants, but much of their capacity to synthesize proteins has been lost. For these latter, or body-building, substances, more than good weather is necessary; plants, like animals, can be said to be, and to behave, only according as they are nourished via the soil.

When the soil fertility declines, our attempts to adapt crops to this lower level of plant nutrition become a fallacy in terms of the demands of the animal diet. Of the many requirements of any diet, protein presents itself for first consideration. In the production of healthy animals the major problem is this one of obtaining sufficient protein of the quality commensurate with nutritional demands. Just as the furnace must be constructed prior to its service in consuming fuel, so must the animal use proteins to build its body prior to any consideration of its expenditure of energy. In the animal the mere hanging on of fat is much of a luxury performance to which we have all want only subscribed.

In agriculture we must become concerned with the biosynthesis of the building stones of the body, namely, the amino acids, making up the proteins and not be content to adopt as our criterion the photosynthesis of the carbohydrates composing the plant bulk.

While this plant bulk may reflect other factors of the environment, we have been able to trace many of our nutritional problems to the effects of the ash constituents coming via the plant. These soil-borne nutrients control plant metabolism more than we yet appreciate. Biosynthesis requires these inorganic elements, not only to catalyze various reactions within the plant, but also to fashion and to build its structure. In turn, animals depend on the plants to synthesize the protein constituents for them. Herein lies the vital function of the soil. According as the different soils deliver divergent quantities of the inorganic elements, so we experience the pattern in the ecological array of the plant species. Each species represents a different organic composition according to the differences in the soil fertility.

In some recent studies, lespedeza was grown on five outlying experiment fields with five different soil types representing the five major soil regions of Missouri. The protein quality of this crop in terms of the different amino acids was assayed by using the newer microbiological techniques. The diversity in the plants' contents of these constituents of the protein molecule manifests itself in going from one soil to another, as shown in Table 1. Here, in terms of the quality of the protein produced through biosynthesis by the plant, we have a more significant yardstick by which to measure our agricultural production according to the different soils, to say nothing of the different products themselves.

In order to determine what fertility elements might be the cause of these diversities, alfalfa was grown on a single soil given treatments of the separate trace elements, manganese and boron, and a mixture of these with some others, as supplements to the common fertilizer elements calcium, phosphorus, and potassium. Wide diversity in the amino acid array in the protein could scarcely be expected when relatively small amounts of these trace elements are applied on the surface of the soil. Yet the quality of the alfalfa protein in terms of its constituent amino acids was modified by these soil treatments, as shown in Table 2. While a marked diversity manifested itself in the case of each amino acid, the methionine content varied most widely of all the amino acids measured in this study. Seemingly these results substantiate the hypothesis that these two trace elements namely, manganese and boron, function in the conversion of the carbohydrate into protein.

Table 1

Amino Acid Content of Lespedeza Hay According to Different Soil Types and Treatments
(Per Cent Dry Weight)

Soil type and treatment	Valine	Leucine	Arginine	Histidine	Threonine	Tryptophane	Lycine	Isoleucine	Methionine
Eldon—treated............	.895	1.055	.646	.375	.632	.294	.992	2.08	.092
untreated..............	.917	.978	.429	.343	.569	.205	.943	1.67	.086
Lintonia—treated........	.922	1.038	.451	.342	.625	.279	.872	1.63	.077
untreated..............	.780	1.014	.329	.306	.544	.181	.878	1.68	.077
Putnam—treated.........	1.023	1.280	.716	.362	.639	.244	.894	1.89	.084
untreated..............	.986	1.289	.563	.503	.606	.227	1.007	2.26	.080
Grundy—treated........	1.010	1.174	.627	.367	.690	.196	.797	2.00	.079
untreated..............	1.137	1.460	.456	.381	.671	.195	.938	2.00	.082
Clarksville—treated......	.853	1.025	.340	.389	.585	.258	.930	1.59	.076
untreated..............	.941	1.199	.367	.356	.557	.215	.870	1.38	.074

Table 2

Amino Acid Content of Alfalfa Hay According to Soil Treatments with Trace Elements
(Percentage of Dry Leaves)

Plot No.	Treatment	Valine	Leucine	Arginine	Histidine	Threonine	Tryptophane	Lycine	Isoleucine	Methionine
1	Calcium.............	2.19	4.37	0.380	0.654	0.862	0.546	1.57	2.64	0.100
2	Calcium and manganese........	2.40	4.89	0.434	0.807	0.954	0.640	2.12	3.63	0.242
3	Calcium and boron..............	2.13	5.55	0.418	0.726	1.071	0.856	2.13	4.09	0.173
4	Calcium and mixture*............	2.59	5.24	0.415	0.835	1.014	0.670	1.87	3.44	0.229

*Mixture of cobalt, copper, zinc, manganese, and boron.

The data in these two tables illustrate well the wide variations in concentrations of these amino acids because of (a) differences in the crops and (b) differences in the fertility of the soils. Since the need to grow protein is greater than that of growing carbohydrates, both for man and animals, here is the suggestion that we should use a more critical measure of our agricultural production—the quality of it according to the fertility of the soil.

A more critical examination of the final crop products is needed. We need to measure not only their physical attributes as bushels and tons but also the amount and quality of their protein, thereby giving fuller consideration to the fertility of the soils on which the products were grown. The diversity of the amino acids within these crops demonstrates clearly that the fertility level of the soil determines our agricultural production in terms of the protein output, which is much more significant than its commonly considered control in terms of only bushels and tonnages. When the national food problem is now looming larger, we believe it is high time to adopt this newer criterion by which to view and direct the creative business that is agriculture.

CHAPTER 20

Wool Quality Depends on Soil Fertility

THE GEOGRAPHIC LOCATION of sheep puts them dominantly on drier soils. Natural survival of them seems to be high in regions of lower rainfall, where soils are less leached of their fertility. Hence, it is on the soils richer in lime, and on grasses grown where calcium and other soil-given nutrients are active in both the soil and the plants, that we find the best reproduction and growth of these producers of both wool and meat. That their wool manufacturing business, like their meat making activities reflect the differences in soil fertility is not so commonly appreciated, even if we have the different breeds for the fine and the coarse wools in different climates and therefore on different soils. But when the same soil in adjoining plots given different fertilizer treatments makes different wool on the back of animals of the same breed, in the scouring vats and in the final carded fibers, we must come to consider the fertility of our soils as a factor in controlling the quality of the wool. Better wool from better soil may be a new slogan to bring the wool producer of the humid region, at least, to consider economic and efficient wool production in terms of soil fertility. This is the suggestion that comes from some experiments testing sheep responses to soil treatments.

In an attempt to use a smaller ruminant than the cow to measure the possible improvement in feeding value of lespedeza hays in consequence of the treatments of superphosphate and lime on the soils growing them, sheep were chosen as the test animal. The lespedeza hay was the legume companion crop of wheat in some of the soil studies of the experiment station. Three plots were involved of which one was given no treatment, one had superphosphate on the wheat at fall seeding, and one the same amount of phosphate but as an addition to limestone on the soil. The wheat was harvested in June and the lespedeza in the stubble made into hay in August to be used as the sheep feed in the dry lots.

Since the plot with no soil treatment produced too little lespedeza hay to carry a significant number of sheep for a good number of days, it could not be used in the first trials. Feeding tests were consequently made with only two lots of lambs. One of these lots was fed on lespedeza hay grown on soil given phosphate, and the other on hay grown where both phosphate and lime were the soil treatments. The grain supplements of corn and bran and all other features of management were the same for the two lots of sheep kept in adjoining pens.

Since the aim was not that of fattening the sheep, but merely one of carrying some weanling lambs through the winter on a moderate amount of feed, only a small daily allotment of grain was given while the hays were fed liberally. The hays were not completely consumed. The unconsumed portion was weighted and careful record kept of the amount taken under a liberal selection by the lambs that left coarser stems and other plant parts. The lambs were put under the experiment on mid-September and carried through until March.

Differences in appearances of the two flocks were detectable before any pronounced differences were shown by the weekly weighings. Those fed on the hay grown where phosphate only was the soil treatment appeared to have cleaner wool, their tops were smoother and there was the general finer wool appearance. Those lambs taking the lespedeza hay grown where both limestone and superphosphate had been the soil treatment appeared as if the wool were not so clean. Their tops were more rough to suggest the effects of more severe weather. These differences persisted and became more pronounced as time passed.

When the animals were given closer study by opening their fleeces, the much more abundant yolk was evident on the rough appearing lambs feeding on the hay grown on the land given lime and phosphate. (Figure 1). The differences in body weights, too, were emphasizing the greater efficiency in animal growth per unit of this hay consumed. When the yearlings were shorn in the spring, samples of wool were collected from the corresponding several parts of the body as the fleeces were weighed and found to be slightly heavier in case of those from the sheep on the hay given both lime and phosphate as the soil treatments.

More significant, however, than any difference in yolk contents of wool, or weights of the fleeces, was the behavior of the wool samples during scouring in dilute alkali solutions. Those from the fleeces with little

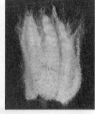

Fig. 1—Differences in the appearance of the wool and in the yolk of the fleeces of the sheep according as they were fed lespedeza hay grown on soil given phosphate only (above) or both lime and phosphate (below).

yolk, or from animals consuming hay grown on soil given phosphate only, seemed to collapse, and appeared as if the fiber were almost a colloidal or jelly-like form. Those samples with much yolk, or from those sheep fed on the hay grown on limestone and superphosphate as the soil treatments, stood up in the scouring liquid to retain their fibrous appearance. When the wool samples were finally rinsed out, carefully air-dried, and carding attempted, those originally with much yolk carded into the usual fluffy, resilient condition of carded wool. Those originally with little yolk coming from the animals given hays with phosphate only could not be carded without breakdown of the fibers.

Here then, is a distinct reflection in the output by the woolmaking part of the sheep. of a decidedly different physiology of those same animals excreting much yolk at the same time they were growing wool on feed from soil stocked with limestone and phosphate. Their output is in contrast to those giving little yolk and wool fibers that did not stand up under scouring in consequence of feeds grown on soil given phosphate but no limestone.

Difference in wool quality in these cases was not due to a difference in breed, nor to a difference in animal age, and not to a difference in plant variety in the feed. It was due to a difference in the soil fertility occasioned by so little as the few hundred pounds of superphosphate combined with the few thousand pounds of limestone put on the millions of pounds of soil per acre. These changes in the physiology of the life of the soil came through as changes in the physiology of the same kind of plants as hay, as changes in the physiology of the sheep eating it, and as decided differences in the quality of the product for which sheep are particularly grown, namely, the wool.

We have not concerned ourselves too seriously about the soil fertility needed to grow animals, when we are thinking of simply going to extensive pasture farming as a soil conservation measure intended to master the problem of soil erosion. Erosion is most serious in regions of high rainfall. It is disastrous in soils that have been cleared of their original timber crops. It is devastating on these soils that are naturally already leached of their lime and other fertility elements, and that have their much more leached and much less fertile subsoils coming up through erosion to be the surface soils. It is on just such soils where much of the pasture farming is to be the rejuvenation for the farms and is to present a new economy by means of animals harvesting the crop cover hopefully saving the soil.

We need to remind ourselves that sheep, like cattle are most prolific and productive with minimum of attention in the regions of lower rainfalls and where the soils are still amply stocked with lime and corresponding mineral plant and animal nutrients. It is in what may well be called the "Midlands of the U.S." that prize animals are produced. It is on the regions of rainfall so low as to make short grass that sheep are well nourished on pastures. It was on these same areas that "Buffalo grass" abounded, or that more scanty vegetation on which the buffalo located his herds and survived. If extra tonnage of feed per acre or minimum of roam to gather it had been his objective surely he would have left the short grass country and gone eastward into the bluestem regions.

Natural animal distributions are pointing to the differences in the fertility of the soil as the basis for the differences in nutritional services of the forages to the animals. Soil treatments in the more humid regions are helping us to understand that it is animal nutrition that determined the distribution. They are demonstrating that animal reproduction, animal growth, and animal output of their products such the wool of the sheep depend on the fertility of the soil reflected in the feed. The animals are, and perform as they are fed. Feeding is not so much a matter of large amounts consumed, but a matter of the quality of the feed taken which as hays and forages goes back to the fertility of the soil where they grew. Wool is an animal crop and in the last analysis, it comes from the soil too. Its quality, therefore, depends on the soil fertility.

CHAPTER 21

Proves Weedy Pastures Lack in Plant Food

ENEMY INVASIONS THREATEN not only our seashores but the agricultural center deep within our continent, for it is here—far inland—that weed enemies are a serious threat to the productivity of our pastures, thereby endangering our meat and milk supplies.

Defense against this form of unsuspected sabotage has not yet been fully organized. Some thought might be given to making our pasture herbages more than a step-child in the list of crops. Are we ready to admit that our soils are sick and for that reason no longer immune to weeds? If this invasion of weeds into our pastures is to be halted, it is essential that we think of treating our soils to make them healthy enough to grow healthy, desirable pasture grasses and these so abundantly that weeds can have no place in the competition.

A 55-Year Record

That healthy soils are immune to weed infestation, while sick soils are readily susceptible, is illustrated clearly by two plots on Sanborn field of the college of agriculture here, one of the oldest fields given to experimental studies of soils. These two plots have been in timothy now for the entire fifty-five years since the field was established. One has been given six tons of barn yard manure annually. The other has had no soil treatment but has been kept simply in this grass crop.

In order to help the latter maintain itself more distinctly in timothy, and to keep it from being completely overrun by all kinds of weeds that were always gradually creeping in, the soil was plowed and reseeded with timothy about ever six or eight years. The adjoining plot given manure annually and in good timothy without weeds was, of course, also plowed and reseeded at the same time. The last plowing and reseeding occurred eight years ago. Here is a form of permanent grass cover, maintained as a fine, long-season, pure crop with manure additions in one case and maintenance attempted only by reseeding in the other case with no soil treatments whatever. In this contrast there is offered the experience of fifty-five years to illustrate the immunity against weeds in the former case and complete infestation by weeds in the latter.

From Grass to Weeds

During the year 1943 the plot without soil treatment changed its flora and shifted from what had once been a timothy plot to a complete stand of broom sedge (or beard grass). This plant, that marks out unproductive soil areas by waving its brown, 2-foot wisps in the winter wind in pastures where cattle have eaten short all the other grasses but have left this plant untouched, is telling us that the soil is now at a low productive level. It is a crop animals really do not eat. It reports that as a pasture this soil has truly "run out."

Why did this weed infestation attack only this one plot in the field of some forty plots? Why did not broom sedge take the adjoining companion plot where manure has been given annually? Surely the evil scatterer did not fail to put some of the same sedge seeds on the manured soil alongside the infested plot or even on the other plots of this old field. If we as humans can be "well fed and healthy" against infectious diseases, can't we imagine that a soil, too, might in some similar manner be "well fed and healthy" and keep its timothy crop while holding out against infestation by weeds?

Food for the Microbes

Perhaps putting manure on annually is a form of giving the soil some extra chemical or mineral fertility to feed the microbes within it. Such additions give it more life. This greater life is an integral part of the soil's internal physiological performances by which the mineral reserves of the soil are changed and delivered in larger amounts to the timothy plants that keep growing continually throughout the season. With vigorous and healthy timothy plants on the healthy soil, there is little chance for such soil to become infested even by such vigorous weed invaders as the broom sedge.

Perhaps manure contributes some animal products, some unknown compounds, or hormone-like substances that benefit the grass crop through the soil. In constructing what has been called the biotic pyramid by Mr. Leopold of Wisconsin, we have the soil supporting the microbes and above them the plants and they in turn supporting animals and then the humans on top. Perhaps there are not only contributions coming from below upward in this pyramidal structure, but possibly there are influences coming from above downward.

It is not beyond possibility that something of a hormone similarity from the animal manures may be helping the timothy to maintain itself and to smother out weeds that might start from chance seedings. At any rate the timothy receiving animal manure—and with it these mineral, chemical or microbial additions—has held its own ground against broom sedge infestation. In contrast the adjoining plot without manure was taken over so completely by broom sedge in a single season that this weed crop grew to seed stage and produced a tonnage of vegetation equivalent to 3,700 pounds per acre. With this weed, as A. W. Klemme's studies show for others, tonnages per acre can be high even after the plot had been cut at haying time.

Merely going to grass is not the solution for our soil erosion problem, nor will it be the introduction of ourselves to a pastoral agriculture. Sanborn Field testifies that merely going to grass may mean going to weeds which the animals know better than to eat. Invasions by weeds are not so much a matter of seed introductions. They are a matter of declining and neglected soil fertility which must be corrected if our pastures are to carry through long grazing seasons with nutritious herbage.

CHAPTER 22

Some Rates
of Fertility Decline

JUST HOW RAPIDLY the fertility of a soil is declining may be as baffling as the question concerning the opposite effect, how rapidly a soil can be built up. To the latter we can only reply, "Very slowly." To the former, we must, unfortunately, answer "Very rapidly."

As a consequence of the rapid decline in fertility and the slow rate of its restoration, the more productive soil areas under cultivation are shrinking. Land is being taken out of production faster than we desire. Some suggested rates of fertility decline are coming to us from farmer experience and from soil-crop studies. They are putting the rate of disappearance of the soil fertility more nearly on a time basis. They are giving answers in numbers of years by which we may well look into the future. Unfortunately, however, these numbers of years before yields will be put below continuance of economic production are much smaller than we like to have them.

Pastures Decline Rapidly

Perhaps one would not expect that pastures are recording very accurately a high rate of soil fertility decline, when so much emphasis is being put upon grass for protection against erosion. But pastures are usually the less fertile soil areas of the farm. It is for this reason that such soils are not put into tilled crops, but are commonly put to, or left in, grass. Naturally, we have no accurate measure, like bushels of grain, of the decline over the years in the fertility under grass. However, when one takes inventory of the increasing incidence of weeds—which incidence of a crop that the cow won't eat is the reciprocal of the disappearance of good grass that

Fig. 1—Continuous timothy since 1888 with regular applications of manure is still making good hay (left), but without manure it is taken by broom sedge (right). Upper photo—before blooming; lower photo—during blooming.

the cow takes readily—there are accumulating data in terms of years to tell us how rapidly the fertility is being pushed down below the level needed for cow-satisfying herbage.

The incidence of broom sedge *(Andropogon virginicus)* is one of these indicators. Its advance over the country from the East toward the West has been considered alarming by some folks. Its increasing prominence in late autumn during its ripening and scattering of seed and its fuzzy whiteness that makes its name "Old Man's Beard" very appropriate have caused extensive concern. That it is not eaten by the livestock and that it remains as a tall growth in the pasture through the winter tell us that its food value is so low that it will not even tempt animals. There is the suggestion, then, that in her refusal to eat broom sedge the cow is reporting on the rate of the decline of soil fertility. She is telling us that the soil, which once made feeds for her, is now making only bulk of no feed value according to her judgment.

The transition from a virgin soil supporting good permanent timothy to one with only broom sedge may be measured as years from the records of Sanborn Field at the University of Missouri. Two plots there have been in timothy continuously since 1888. One of these had no soil treatment except that of being plowed out and reseeded when the overseer thought it was so foul with weeds that reseeding was necessary. It has been in this grass continuously with no more attention than the annual hay harvest. The other plot alongside, also in timothy, has been given six tons of manure annually. It has been plowed each time that it was necessary to plow the weedy companion plot in order to keep the tillage treatments of these two plots alike.

The plot given manure up to this date has not yet suffered from the incidence of weeds. On the plot with no treatment, the seeding of timothy lasts now scarcely two years before weeds take over. In 1945 the broom sedge had completely taken this plot. But the broom sedge had not crossed the border lines to the adjoining timothy plot alongside given manure, nor had it gone to the roadways at the ends in continuous bluegrass.

Even this timothy, now for less than 60 years, has exhausted the fertility to the point where reseeding fails to hold much of this crop past the year of seeding. Here was cropping to a grass agriculture for but a little more than half a century to tell us that even this much-publicized system of farming for a permanent cover to guard against the erosive effects of running water needs more than merely this special system of cropping. It is suggesting that any system of cropping must be undergirded by a regular and generous flow of fertility from (a) the organic matter in decay, or (b) the exchangeable store adsorbed on the colloid, or (c) the breakdown of the mineral reserves. It is directing attention to the fertility flow that is keeping well filled those assembly lines of agriculture hidden away within the soil.

Mesquite Crowds Out Grass

The westward march of mesquite *(Prosopis glandulosa)* across the Southwest Plains to occupy what was once considered good range pastures is an other trouble, equally as disturbing as the weed problem in the fenced pastures. While the mowing machine and hormone sprays may be consolation to some folks worried about the weeds in the pastures, such tools and treatments can scarcely be feasible helps on the extensive range areas going to mesquite so completely and so speedily.

The Forest Service has cited the short time of 40 years in the Santa Rita Mountains, with their low annual rainfall, as the time required to exhaust the soil fertility by only grazing, and to push the soil's productivity down from good range for cattle to mesquite brush. Here again the figure is near the half century mark. It is small, even under the livestock system of using

Fig. 2—Grasses went out and mesquite took over on these ranges in the Santa Rita Mountains in less than a half century. Upper photo—1903; lower photo—1943.

the land, and is the lifetime of the fertility supply at the respectable nutritive level of the short grass and its limited production of vegetative bulk.

The Decline of Tilled Soil

Under tillage, the decline of the fertility of the soil would be expected to be more rapid. But even under such treatment, one cannot arrive at the longevity of the productivity by considering only the system of land use. Here too, the flow of fertility from the assembly lines of the soil determines the number of years it can hold out under the cropping pressure. Once more Sanborn Field, but this time under continuous wheat, gives some duration figures as years from its plot with no fertility return—not even the straw—since 1888.

This plot demonstrated a gradual decline of wheat yields from 1888 on ward for almost 40 years before its nearly complete crop failures became so evident. These crop failures have now become almost regular occurrences in alternate years since 1925. Here are some suggestions: (a) That the virgin supply of soil organic matter is almost completely exhausted, with the former store of actively decaying humus no longer helping much to make the seed crops, (b) that the mineral reserves in their breakdown are contributing at a rate too slow for annual crops, and (c) that the clay colloid is not restocked with exchangeable nutrients by the October seeding after the crop's exhaustion of them in the preceding July harvest.

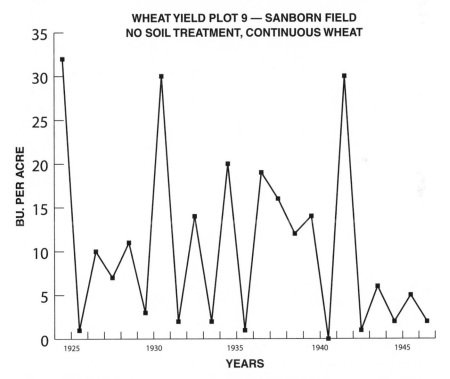

Fig. 3—The soil growing wheat continuously without treatment since 1888 on Sanborn Field, Columbia, Missouri, has become an alternate-year bearer during the last 20 years. The graph of the annual yields drops almost to zero in regular alternate years since 1925.

In the case of the continuous wheat, like the cases for the pastures and the ranges, the nearly half century of regular productivity was the limit given us for this prairie soil prevailing in northeast Missouri. After less than a half century this soil became what might be called an alternate-year bearer, or a regular biennial reproducer, because of the insufficient flow of the essential inorganic nutrients from the soil. The decline in the supply of soil fertility during but a half century has recorded itself as a failure in the crop to reproduce itself as even the equivalent of the necessary seed, and then only when seed from outside sources for this plot was used.

Do such records have any implications for tree crops as well as for grain crops when we remind ourselves that it is the older apple trees that become "alternate-year," or "biennial" bearers of apple crops while young trees are annual bearers? When older cows become "shy breeders" can the decreasing soil fertility under their feed crops possibly be the indirect factors in the case?

Quite contrary to expectations and common claims for rotations in the up-keep of soil fertility, the crops in even the 6-year rotation are now down to failure on the plot given no soil treatment. This is true although corn, oats, and wheat are only three tilled crops out of six in the rotation, and each has been grown now only 10 times since the soil was put under cultivation. The clover has been failing for a quarter of a century. The timothy occupying the land for two years in the rotation has been little more than tickle grass. Rotation with no more help from the clover and sod during three years of the six was little or no different than the continuous wheat in the rate of decline of the soil fertility. Without soil treatments of manure, lime and other fertilizers, and regardless of whether continuous sod, continuous tilled cropping, or any length of rotation going as long as six years, the supply of fertility on Sanborn Field is approaching exhaustion in nearly half a century.

Task of Future Restoration

Reproduction by the plant from seed is not a matter of only the starch in it, except as this is reserve energy for the germ that is rich in protein and many other compounds. For the synthesis of these complex components representing potential reproduction, the fertility of the soil, more than the weather, is demanded. Troubles in reproduction in plants and animals are the reflection of the declining fertility supply in the soil. Shrinking lifetimes of our fields are the underlying causes of much that has not yet been traced to this as the cause. Better reproduction can come only as we minister to the soil, which is the source of the entire process of creation. If creation of food as plants and animals is to continue abundantly in the future, we can scarcely guarantee its projection there without being guided by the records of the past concerning the rates of decline of the soil fertility.

CHAPTER 23

Biosynthesis of Amino Acids According to Soil Fertility, Bioassays of Forage & Grain Fertilized with "Trace" Elements

THAT FERTILIZATION OF the soil brings about improvement in the nutritional values of feed as measured by animal growths, was reported by Albrecht and Smith; McLean; and Kendall, Nevens and Overman. When the problem of nutrition points to the proteins, not only in totals measured by nitrogen but also in the proper balance of their constitutent essential amino acids, then, the synthesis of these nitrogenous compounds by plants (and microbes) for higher nutritional values in forages and grains for animals may well be considered as a responsibility of proper soil management. That the concentrations of various amino acids in plants are influenced by the different inorganic nutrient elements and the ratios of their concentrations in the medium in which the plants are grown was shown by Sheldon, Blue, and Albrecht. The work reported here was another attempt to study this relation of the amino acid array in a forage (alfalfa, or lucerne) and in a grain (corn or maize) to the soil treated with "trace" as well as major elements of fertility values. It was an attempt, also to make bioassays of the forage and the grain by means of rabbits with even amino acid- and other nutritional-supplements in the rations for these test animals.

Experimental Methods

The forage crop of alfalfa (lucerne) was grown on a residual limestone soil (Newtonia silt loam) in Southwest Missouri, (U.S.A.), given four soil treatments. These were: (1) magnesium sulfate (100 pounds/acre) plus a trace element mixture at the same rate; (2) magnesium sulfate only; (3) no treatment; and (4) trace elements (100 pounds/acre). The mixture of the trace elements contained manganese sulfate, 55 pts; copper sulfate, 20 pts; borax (sodium tetraborate), 10 pts; zinc sulfate, 10 pts; and cobalt sulfate, 5 pts.

Chemical analyses of the samples of four alfalfa hays grown on the soils given these different treatments were made for the elements nitrogen, calcium, magnesium, phosphorus, potassium, sodium, and copper. The hays were subjected to microbiological analyses for nine of the ten amino acids essential for the white rat (phenyl alanine was not determined). They were then subjected to a bioassay of their nutritional values by feeding them to four groups of young, white, New Zealand rabbits. Some of the rabbits were fed *ad libitum* and some were *pair fed*. All of them were given a supplement of ten grams of oats per head per day.

The grain crop of corn (maize) was grown on one of the planosols (Cherokee silt loam) also in Southwest Missouri (U.S.A.) in a test using each of seven different combinations of the five major elements (nitrogen, phosphorus, potassium, calcium, and magnesium) as fertilizers in conjunction with each of three rates, viz. 0, 100, and 300 pounds per acre of the trace element mixture. Tests were made of (a) the hardness of the grains on grinding, (b) the rabbits' preference for them in lots of seven, (c) the amounts of each of the ten essential amino acids they contained according to microbiological assays, and (d) nutritional values by feeding some of them from different soil treatments to rabbits, with and without supplements of the commonly deficient three amino acids, viz. lysine, tryptophane, and methionine, and of vitamins and casein.

Results from Trials of the Forage

In the chemical studies of the alfalfa (lucerne) hays, the major differences in their relation to the fertility treatments of the soil growing them were found for the concentrations of phosphorus and for some of the amino acids. Although the concentrations of total nitrogen in the alfalfa varied but little with the soil treatments the concentrations of the tryptophane and the methionine in the hay were increased by the addition of magnesium and trace elements in combination (Table 1). The fact that these two amino acids are most commonly deficient in many forages gives particular significance to this discovery. When fed the hays grown on the soil treated with magnesium plus the trace elements, the rabbits made better gains by 15 per cent than those by the rabbits fed the hay grown with no soil treatments (Table 2). Twenty-two per cent less hay was required per unit of gain in the former case than in the latter (Table 2).

Table 1

Concentrations of Nitrogen, Phosphorus, and Two Amino Acids in Alfalfa Hay According to Treatments of the Soil Growing it.

Treatments of the Soil	Concentrations			
	Nitrogen (%)	Phosphorus (%)	Tryptophane (mg/g)	Methionium (mg/g)
Magnesium and trace elements...............	3.05	0.247	2.52	5.44
Magnesium...............	3.20	0.224	—	—
No treatment............	3.12	0.218	1.86	4.57
Trace elements...........	3.19	0.211	—	4.20

It is significant that the forage grown on the soil given the treatments consisting of magnesium alone, or of only the mixture of the five trace elements (manganese, copper, boron, zinc, and cobalt), gave (a) no significant increase in the concentrations of the commonly deficient amino acids in the forage; (b) no greater gains in rabbit weights; and (c) no significantly greater gains per unit of feed consumed than those from the forage grown on the soil given no treatment. However, when two of these treatments of the soil were combined, i.e. applying the magnesium along with the five trace elements, then the forage was improved decidedly (a) in its concentrations of tryptophane and methionine, (b) in the gains in the weights of rabbits in a given time, (c) and in the gains per unit of feed consumed.

What this all would mean in terms of the fecundity of the rabbits was not studied. It suggests, however, that research in plant nutrition would be more remunerative if, instead of using each element singly as a soil treatment and then these in various combinations of a few of the essential elements, all the known elements were applied in combination and then in successive trials an individual one, or combinations of them, were witheld in the manner similar to that used in studies in human nutrition testing the amino acids. It suggests still further, that the soil treatments can improve the nutritional values of the forages for animals, and that these improvements probably come via the better balance of the amino acids and other complex compounds of synthetic origin within the plants.

Table 2

Gains in Weights and Alfalfa Hays Consumed Per Gram of Gain by Rabbits According as Hays Fed Them were Grown on Soils Given Different Treatments.

	Gains (G/Animal)			Hay		
	Ad lib. Feed	Paired Feed	Av.	Offered G/Animal	Wasted G/An.	Consumed G/G Gain
Magnesium and trace elements	879	809	849	4536	1105	4.04
Magnesium	742	748	744	5050	1561	4.69
No treatment	751	711	740	5084	1491	4.86
Trace elements	684	723	699	4840	1420	4.89

Results from Trials with the Grain

While, naturally, one cannot know how corn tastes to a rabbit and cannot design methods of measuring the differences in tastes, it seemed that possibly the hardness of the corn grain might be a factor in the rabbits' preference for that from one soil treatment over another when their selection from a lot was permitted. Accordingly, the respective hardnesses of the samples of corn from the twenty-one different soil treatments were determined by running each through a Wiley laboratory mill and sieving it with a nest of 10-, 40-, and 80-mesh sieves to find the percentages of the samples passing through each.

There was the least variation in hardness of the grain for the seven combinations of the major nutrient elements without additions of the trace elements as soil treatments. For this lot from 14.7 to 21.3 per cent passed through the 10-mesh sieve. But when 100 and 300 pounds, or increasing amounts, of trace elements supplemented the major nutrient elements applied to the soil, then there was greater variation in the hardness of the grains, namely, from 14.3 to 30.7 and from 8.1 to 33.7 per cent, respectively, passing the 10-mesh sieve.

But when these samples of grain were submitted to the rabbits in lots according to the seven major nutrient elements as the only variable while the soil treatment with trace elements was a constant, the variations in the amounts consumed showed the maximum taken over the minimum amounting to 1.25 times for zero trace elements, 2.3 times for 100 pounds of these applied to the soil, and 2.05 times for their application at 300 pounds per acre in combination with the major nutrients. That there was no correlation between the hardness as measured by grinding and the selection by the rabbits as shown by amounts consumed in these lots, was clearly demonstrated by the fact that these animals consumed exactly the same amounts of the hardest and of the softest of the samples. Surely, then, the differentiation by the rabbits between these grains was not according to their hardness as measured by the extra labor of grinding of mastication, but was according to the other differences invoked by differences in the soil treatments.

It was significant that as an average, in this preference testing of the lots of grain when the major nutrients as soil treatments varied with a single trace element treatment in combination, the amounts of grain consumed as a lot were highest for the soil treatments using no trace elements, the next highest were for the 300 pounds of this treatment, and lowest for the soil treatment with 100 pounds of trace elements as supplementary fertilizer. When the heaviest applications of the trace elements to the soil (300 lbs/A) were considered, it was significant that the rabbit preference, in terms of maximum grain consumption, singled out this soil treatment of the trace elements, in some cases of it in combination with or without the major elements accompanying it. This latter choice was confirmed by field observations when the grain on the plot with only 300 pounds of trace elements was taken by rodents much more than that on any other plot, and by the fact that among the twenty-one bags in storage, the mice cut into only the bag representing this particular soil treatment of trace elements alone and in their heavy applications.

In a second trial, in which the major nutrient elements were nearly a constant soil treatment while the trace elements were the variable and the consumption of grain represented the rabbits' choice between 0, 100, and 300 pounds of the trace elements as soil treatments, the preference by them was (a) for the corn fertilized with 100 pounds of trace elements when these three rates each were combined with only dolomite or with dolomite and starter fertilizers; (b) for no trace elements when in conjunction with most complete major nutrient fertilization; (c) for 100 pounds of these when the complete fertilization used superphosphate in place of rock phosphate; and (d) for 100 pounds of trace elements when in combination with more complete major treatments omitting potassium; but for 300 pounds of trace elements when these were used alone. As an average, the preference pointed to the 100 pounds of trace elements in these three sets of combinations according to 0, 100, and 300 pounds of trace elements.

While the selections of the grains by the rabbits, or their preferences for consumption, presented marked discriminations according to the treatments of the soil growing the grains, such preferences pointed to no particular physiological factor as possibly responsible. Consequently, the corn grains were fed to lots of rabbits (4–7 per lot) for six weeks with the corn supplemented by amounts of (a) each of the pure amino acids separately; namely, tryptophane, .11–.12 per cent by weight; methionine, .23–.30 per cent; and lysine .20 per cent, (b) vitamins* and (c) casein 5 per

---

* With each 400g corn there were added:

5000 units	— Vitamin A
1000 units	— Vitamin D
2.5 mg	— Vitamin B_1 (Thiamine hydrochloride)
2.5 mg	— Vitamin B_2 (Riboflavin)
50.0 mg	— Vitamin C (Ascorbic acid)
20.0 mg	— Nicotinamide (Niacinamide)
5.0 mg	— Pantothenic Acid (Calcium salt)
0.5 mg	— Vitamin B_8 (Pyridoxine hydrochloride)
1.0 mcg	— Vitamin B_{12} (Cyanocobalamin)

Table 3

Concentrations of Total Nitrogen, Lysine, Tryptophane and Methionine in Corn (Maize) According to Soil Treatments Growing it, and Gains in Weights by Rabbits Consuming it With and Without Supplements

No. Soil treatment	Treatment	Nitrogen %	Lysine mg/g	Tryptopha-ne mg/g	Methionine mg/g	Supplement Fed	Gain/Rab. G/6wks	G Corn/ G Gain
1	Magnesium limestone	1.61	10.0	0.60	5.7	None	291	5.48
2	Treatment 1 plus starter fert. (a)....	1.58	8.8	0.74	5.0	—	—	
3	Treatment 2 plus nitrogen, pot. rock phos. and trace ele. (b)	1.81	7.0	0.67	5.9	Tryptophane Methionine (c) Lysine	281	5.59
4	Treatment 3 plus extra trace ele. (d) and superphos	1.79	10.0	0.69	4.9	None	129	13.67
5	Treatment 4	1.79	10.0	0.69	4.9	Methionine	204	6.53
6	Treatment 3 minus potassium	1.72	7.0	0.56	5.7	None	175	8.28
7	Treatmemt 6	1.72	7.0	0.56	5.7	Tryptophane	260	5.31

Continued

Table 3 (Continued)

Concentrations of Total Nitrogen, Lysine, Tryptophane and Methionine in Corn (Maize) According to Soil Treatments Growing it, and Gains in Weights by Rabbits Consuming it With and Without Supplements

No. Soil treatment	Treatment	Nitrogen %	Lysine mg/g	Tryptophane mg/g	Methionine mg/g	Supplement Fed	Gain/Rab. G/6wks	G Corn/ G Gain
8	None	1.78	7.9	0.62	5.7	None	202	7.97
9	Treatment 8	1.78	7.9	0.62	5.7	Vitamins (e)	233	6.79
10	Treatment 8 plus trace elements ..	1.62	7.9	0.59	5.4	None	212	5.72
11	Treatment 10	1.62	7.9	0.59	5.4	Casein (f)	344	4.30

(a) The starter fertilizer used as the soil treatment consisted of 250 lbs per acre of a 4-12-4.

(b) The complete soil treatment consisted of the starter fertilizer, after plowing under per acre 400 lbs ammonium nitrate, 200 lbs potassium chloride, 1500 lbs rock phosphate and trace elements, 100 lbs.

(c) These three amino acids were added in pure form since in respect to the commonly considered needs for rats the corn was seriously low in these amino acids.

(d) The trace elements in total amounted to 300 lbs per acre, while other treatments were the duplicate of treatment No. 3.

(e) This was a composite of many vitamins. (See footnote on previous page).

(f) Purified casein was a supplement to the extent of five per cent of the ration.

cent. The gains in weight by the rabbits, and the corn required per gram of gain, as given in Table 3, show clearly that the soil treatments growing the corn exerted a decided effect on the nutritional efficiency of the grain as measured by the gains in weight of the rabbits.

Of the treatments using only the major elements on this soil, the dolomitic, or magnesium, limestone was most singular in giving corn of high nutritional efficiency when it required but 5.48 grams to make a gram of gain in weight of rabbit. The treatment next in the decreasing order of efficiency was the trace elements only, when 5.72 grams of corn were required per gram of gain. Corn grown without any treatment required almost eight grams, 7.97, to make one gram of rabbit gain. When heavy soil treatments of major elements were used omitting potassium, it required 8.28 grams of corn for one of gain. But when the major five elements, including superphosphate in place of rock phosphate, and the extra trace elements were the soil treatments growing the corn grain, it required 13.67 grams of corn per gram of gain in body weight.

That these efficiencies could be improved by the addition of (a) some of the more commonly deficient amino acids, (b) the more complete protein (casein), and (c) the vitamins, is clearly indicated by the greater nutritional efficiency of the corn when these supplements were fed along with it. That the trace elements alone and the dolomitic limestone, all not commonly considered effective for increasing the yields as bushels per acre, served to improve the nutritional efficiency is not only startling, but also significant. It suggests that we have been led astray from nutritional services as the objective in growing this grain. That the fertilizer treatments with major elements, commonly considered most beneficial for increased yields as bushels of grain per acre, should have been so inefficient in giving the grain nutritional values is even more startling. That grain so grown should compel an animal to eat 2.5 times the amount to make the gain possible when eating corn grown on the same soil treated with only dolomitic limestone, points clearly to our past management of the soil for the delivery of vegetative bulk but not necessarily for nutritional efficiency by that mass produced.

These results show that by means of bioassays of our forages and grains, we shall be able to manage our soils more judiciously to produce these feeds for efficient nutritional services, and to recognize the benefits by magnesium, by the trace elements and, by other aspects of soil fertility not yet, or only recently, given attention as beneficial additions to the soil.

CHAPTER 24

Buy More Fertilizer but Less Feed

MORE DOLLARS OF net profits result from more tons of higher quality feed grown right on the farm. When we think of hay we measure it in tons. When the cow measures the feed value of the hay she is judging it in terms of both quality and quantity. Accordingly as the quality of it is higher, her output goes up per unit of our measures of it.

An increasing number of farmers of Missouri are appreciating the fact that the quality of hay goes up as the fertility of the soil growing it goes higher. They are learning that hay to be had for purchase may not be of the same high quality they can grow on their own fertilized soils. They are building up the agriculture of the state by building up the soils in fertility that supports it. They are taking, therefore, to buying more lime and other fertilizers as indicated by the increased amounts used during the last few years. As a consequence they are purchasing less feeds; feeds that all too often are those some one believes to be too poor to give to his own livestock.

Such was the thinking back of the changes in his farm management that were brought about by Jess Mennick, Dallas County, Missouri. He began his operations six years ago on his own farm. This was purchased by help from the Farm Security Administration in the hope that his ten Jersey cows, as his principal source of income, would keep his family and liquidate his financial obligations in attempting to provide future security for it.

In going over the records at the close of the year, he and his supervisor came to the belief that he was spending what looked like an excessive sum for hay. Each year Mr. Mennick had thought that it would be the last one in which he would be forced to buy this extra feed. But he was about convinced that his farm would not raise all the hay he needed. Yet the hay he was purchasing was of questionable quality. He recognized the drop in milk flow when his cows went on it. He knew it was what other men had left over and what was grown on the areas of low fertility in the neighborhood. He finally came to the conclusion that he would grow his own forages and would improve them in quality—as well as get more quantity—by means of more fertilizer and lime treatments on his soil.

Mr. Mennick is now on a program of growing all the hay he needs. It was in the year 1945 that he made the shift from the necessity of buying feeds to the assurance of having surplus feeds. The use of almost a ton more of fertilizer was the main contributing factor that pushed the balance sheet of his feed account from the debit to the credit side. Here is the summary in brief of the swing-over in the records as it occurred:

Table 1

*Summary of Mennick Farm Feed
and Milk Produced in 1945.*

Fertilizer purchased, lbs.	4,500
Expenses for purchased hay	00
Milk produced, lbs.	74,500
Cows, milked	10
Grazing arrangement:	
wheat pastured, acres	15
sweet clover, acres	8
sudan, acres	7
Earnings per hour for his labor	1.25

Mr. Mennick had in his barn on the inventory date in 1946 twenty-one tons of hay grown at home. On that date the preceding year he had six tons that had been hauled in as purchased. He appreciates the higher quality of his own hay as compared to purchased hay. He reports that as a consequence of this better quality in the hay and the grazing, his heifers have been developing better than in any previous time. They come to a better flow of milk with their first calves. His cows shed better in the spring and troubles at calving time are reduced.

Mr. Mennick is convinced that what may look like a shift in management to save the expense of purchased hay, in reality provides greater financial returns in the better foundation for production on the farm as a whole, namely the more fertile soil. He is buying more lime and other fertilizers because he grows not only more feed but better feed in terms of what it takes to have the cows make calves and more milk. For him the buying of fertilizers is better business than the buying of more feed.

CHAPTER 25

The Soil as the Basis of Wildlife Management

WILDLIFE IS A CROP of the land. It is a crop just as are grass, corn, wheat, calves, pigs and other creations in the form of plants and animals under domestication. We grant readily that the size of a crop, like corn, for example, depends on the fertility of the soil growing it. We select better land for a better crop, and we fertilize a given piece of land to improve the crop from it. Unfortunately, we have not thought much about controlling the animal crop, whether domestic or wildlife, by selecting, managing, and fertilizing the soil. We have planted and transplanted both plants and animals, all too haphazardly, from one place of their generous production in suitable habitat to most any other place with little more than a simple, blind faith in the species to guarantee its own survival. We have been too reluctant to believe that the failures of such transplanting may be provoked by the infertility of the soil making the new habitat unsuitable. We speak of a certain region as "good cattle country", or "good sheep country", or "good quail country", or as a region of "fine rabbit shooting". We see the animal crop there. We see the crops of grain, the rainfall, the snows, and other environmental features, but we fail to see the underlying soil and its fertility as the basic control of what kinds of plants will grow and thereby what food for wildlife any region provides.

Dependence on Soils Seems More Remote by Some Wildlife

Wildlife includes many animal groups differing in their feeding habits and in the degree of dependence directly on the soil. In simpler classification, there are the carnivorous, the omnivorous and the herbivorous, which

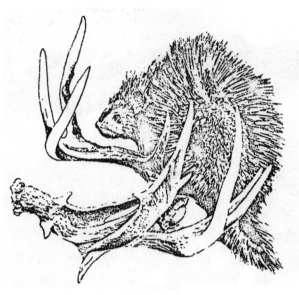

Fig. 1—Wildlife struggles desparately to find the necessary calcium and phosphorus coming out of the soil to make bones, when antlers are quickly consumed by the porcupine, the pregnant squirrels, and other animals living on the highly weathered forest soils.

is the order as we might see them more closely connected with the soil. We have not yet studied the herbivora in sufficient detail to see how their grazing is limited to certain soil types or to specific soil areas, and how the patterns of their concentration and distribution are determined by the fertility of the soil and thereby are in accordance with the climatic forces developing it. The fact that the buffalo selected the Chernozem and Chestnut soils with their short prairie grasses, where today we grow the "hard" or the high-protein wheat and many of our cattle of good meat-producing quality, is an excellent illustration of one of the many cases where the soil pattern was in control of wildlife. That same soil pattern is likewise controlling the patterns for domestic animal and human life today.

The carnivorous animals too must fit into the pattern of the soil fertility as it provides them food. However, they are farther removed—mainly in our thinking—from the soil as the provider of their foods. Fish are highly carnivorous in the tropical seas, but of more omnivorous feeding habits in temperate waters. It is not readily appreciated that carnivorousness is such a common character of all wildlife in the humid tropics, suggesting the necessity of such habits for survival. Nor is carnivorousness connected with the fact that high rainfalls and high temperatures give exhausted soils and only forests, of which the vegetative bulk can scarcely be as nutritious as are the short grasses growing on the semi-arid, highly fertile soils capable of feeding the massive-bodied buffaloes. Carnivorousness is the predominant habit whenever the animals can't support themselves by feeding more directly on the soil and when they must therefore feed on each other. Herbivorousness, or subsistence more directly on the products of the soil, is predominant where lower rainfalls and moderate temperatures prevail and thereby provide the more fertile soils and they in turn grow the more nutritious vegetation. The climatic forces determine the kind of soil and thereby the feed, and through it are manifesting their control therefore seemingly less directly. Different animals are in specific climatic conditions more because of the food produced by the soil developed under those climatic forces than because of the comfort to animals in terms of suitable temperature and moisture.

Soil Fertility is a Pattern for Management of Any Kind of Wildlife

The management of wildlife is giving emphasis to feeding as the dominant factor by which the wildlife crop can be produced and preserved on lands that are marginal for domestic crops. Under its own efforts for survival in competition with man's encroachments on its range, wildlife is rapidly being pushed into its reluctantly accepted therritories that are bringing about its slow extinction. Its survival demands its submission to man's management and to his provision of foods and feeds in the habitats that will truly nourish these animals for their reproduction. Wildlife is not greatly different from domestic animal life. The soil is coming to be recognized more and more as the support via foods for all life forms now that the depletion of the fertility of our soils is marking out the areas of both crop and animal extinction and is delineating more sharply the soil areas of their survival. Land areas are being studied from a new viewpoint, now that even we of the cornbelt of the United States have had a few years of experience in rationing and in food shortages. A given area is no longer merely a site. Like the wild animals, we are reacting to a geographical area with concern for ourselves and for our domestic animals according as it feeds us, or as its soils produce the foods that truly nourish. The soil fertility pattern by which we seek to undergird the growth of crops and domestic animals must be viewed as the same pattern by which the management of our wildlife may be more logical and successful also. Only under the concern by man for his wildlife crop, and not in its competition with him, can our supply of game escape extinction.

Feeding Overshadows Breeding

Prompted probably by the emphasis on breeding in the management of domestic animals, the breeding phase of wildlife management has raised hopes and beliefs that we can crossbreed, for example, one type of male bird or animal on another to increase the capacities for survival. The enthusiasts for the possibilities of genetics seemingly would push our domestic animals and our wildlife into many geographical areas formerly unknown to them. Such aspects as "hybrid vigor" uncovered by breeding trials lend enthusiasm. Hybrid corn, in the case of plants, has gotten more bushels or more bulk per acre. But this has happened (1) not without a seemingly more starchy grain of lower values as protein and lesser feeding power for body growth as Nebraska experiments with chicks indicate, and (2) not without exhausting the soil fertility so speedily that the special advantage of hybrid corn as more bushels per acre shrinks rapidly on successive cropping by it.

In our domestic animals, the mule has also been a similar case of hybrid vigor. But we failed to appreciate the observation that this animal slave of ours has been confined in its birth and growth to regions of highly calcareous soils or areas of low rainfall. We have accused this beast of being stubborn in its strange feeding habits when in fact is was exhibiting a self-regulatory appetite and other characters that are essential for the survival of the mule when forced to be so highly exotic as is true of it, for example, on the cotton soils of our southern states.

A few such cases of particular advantage obtained through genetics is illustrated by hybrid vigor have encouraged trials in other plants and other domestic animals. They have kept alive the hope that some helps may come therefrom to wildlife also and that marvels may be accomplished by manipulating the genes of the reproduction cells. Breeding has, of course, its potentialities. It has, for example, given increased resistance to disease. It has developed tolerations of shortages in many respects. But the toleration of starvation certainly is one character that cannot be established permanently by the most marvelous manipulations of the geneticist. Breeding may do much in determining the mating of the particular male and female cells, but after conception has once occurred, it is then that feeding takes over. It is then that the soil, which grows feeds exercises the main controls. It is essential that we see the soil and its production of feeds as the means of effective management of all wildlife, including all of its breeding variations or characteristics.

Animals Search for Proteins & Minerals

The problems of feeding our domestic animals point out most forcefully that many soils are giving poor feed for our farm animals and would be producers of poor feed for any wild animal of similar feeding habits, Whether it is feeding for milk production, for fattening, for reproduction, or even for only maintenance, it is a necessary and common farm practice on many and extensive regions of soils to supplement the native feed crops with mineral and protein concentrates. Soil management for feed production for domestic animals has long been calling for lime applications to make possible the mineral-rich and more proteinaceous legume crops. These crops are in high demand for the young and growing animals, for the milk producers, and even for fattening without disaster. Our feeding of domestic animals is given distinctly to the struggle of providing enough of the essential minerals of soil-borne origin, and of the proteins built up of the amino acids originating only in synthesis by the plants on the more fertile soils.

Soil Treatments Mean More Proteins & Minerals in Feeds

Our soil treatments practiced most extensively are those which encourage higher concentration of minerals and proteins in the crop. Calcium put on as limestone for the formerly erroneous purpose of fighting soil acidity serves to give a higher concentration of the nutrient calcium within the crop, to bring along with itself a higher concentration of other minerals, and to synthesize more protein by means of more nitrogen taken from both the soil and the atmosphere. Phosphorus also exercises its effects on the better protein synthesis and on the more effective reproduction of the plant through a bigger seed crop. Nitrogen, too, goes as fertilizer for the building of protein in the crop and is the one element by which protein is distinguished in terms of chemical analysis. Soil treatments are not emphasizing the increased production of carbohydrates or fattening foods so much since these are crop functions performed commonly on must any soils. Soil treatments are testimony that it a far greater struggle to have plants provide sufficient minerals and proteins in themselves as feeds. Just as the deficient soils point to the plant's struggle for proteins that make for seeds and plant reproduction so our less fertile soils point to the animal and human struggle, not for carbohydrates or fuel foods of plant photosyntheses, but for the minerals, the proteins and all those complex products of the plant's biosyntheses that build bodies and encourage fecund reproduction.

Animal's Selection of Feed Points to Soil Fertility

That wild animal life in its wide roaming and discriminating selections of its feed should be limited by the soil fertility may seem difficult to believe. It is difficult since plant life above the soil and microbial life within the soil seem a weak force to bind the warm-blooded, physiologically complex behaviors of higher life to the slow, highly inorganic chemical reactions within the cold soil body. Nevertheless, the animal must depend on the soil to provide it with the dozen or more essential nutrient elements found only there where they serve as nourishment also for the microbes and where they determine what creative services the plants can perform in terms of food for wildlife and all other life. It is the differences in the activities within the soil in supplying these dozen or more nutrients that provoke the roamings and the searchings of animals as they select their food so discriminatingly. We are just coming to appreciate the fact that it is the differences in soil fertility and thereby the differences in the quality of the feeds that prompt wild animals to cover their territory and to select their feeds so wisely for their own better survival.

Choices of grazing and other feeds by domestic and wild animals have pointed to the animal's struggle for the soil-borne minerals and the proteins encouraged by them or by minerals and nitrogen applied in fertilizers. In Pennsylvania the deer coming down from the mountains for their winter grazing choose their browse regularly in woodland areas which had been fertilized. When deer are considered a pest we forget that they may be suffering some nutrient deficiencies in consequence of their feeding on vegetation growing on very poor soil and one producing only poor wood. We forget, too, that they may find the means of remedying that deficiency by grazing the crops on our cultivated fields where fertilizers or tillage have remedied that deficiency. Soils that represent no more highly specialized plant processes than merely that of making wood even when all the soil fertility is dropped back annually in the leaves, surely cannot be supplying highly nutritious vegetation. That such is the case is suggested when the browse of deer consists only of the growing buds or tips of the shoots where the maximum concentration of life activity by the plant occurs.

Domestic animals have been observed in many instances to roam and locate a particular soil area according to the fertility of it and according to the higher concentration of protein or of mineral contents of the feed. A Missouri farmer reported that his cattle were eating first the area of barley where 200 pounds of fertilizer were applied but they left ungrazed to the very drill row that where only 100 pounds were used. An Iowa tenant farmer was startled to find his 20 head of cattle grazing on a 20-acre section of an unfenced 300-acres of stalks in the cornfield after husking. This surprise at the animal discrimination was more startling when he connected their behavior with the 70 pounds per acre of nitrogen on the 20-acre strip as special treatment in addition to the 100 pounds of fertilizer per acre on the entire field.

Plowing the soil as a means of releasing soil fertility was sufficient improvement in the feeding quality of bluegrass to make cattle graze it very closely where the land was plowed and reseeded in making waterways while they disregarded the part of the field of bluegrass left unplowed. Native prairie grasses fertilized with calcium and nitrogen in 1936 and put into one of four stacks of hay in the field annually were chosen regularly for nine successive years by cattle in their consumption first of the one particular haystack. Lespedeza hays fertilized with lime and phosphate were selected in the field by cattle and sheep.

Feeds Selected are Higher in Nutritional Values

Such hays put under test as feed for sheep were more efficient lamb producers when phosphate only or lime and phosphate together had been applied to the soils growing this feed. Lespedeza and soybean hays from soil given only phosphatic fertilizers were over 50 percent more efficient in growing body size but also in growing wool of better quality. Wool from sheep fed lespedeza hay grown on soils given only phosphate could not be scoured and carded. When scoured, it consisted of broken fibers in contrast to excellent wool that carded nicely when from sheep fed on hays grown on soil given both lime and phosphate. Such is testimony that the physiology of the sheep depends on the physiology of the plants serving as feed. It is the soil fertility that is the foundation of the physiology or function of all the life dependent on it.

Fecundity of Animals Depends on Soil Fertility

The reproductive processes of the animals under experiment reflected the effects of the soil treatments through the hays. Sheep fed on timothy hay grown on soil given lime were in breeding condition as one-year-olds while those fed the similar hay grown without soil treatment were not. Lespedeza hays grown similarly on the soils with different treatments registered their disturbing influence on the semen production of male rabbits. The hay from soil with no treatment serving as feed for sexually active male rabbits caused them almost to lose the capacity of semen production and induced their indifference to the female in oestrus. When returned to the feedings of lespedeza hay grown on land given lime and phosphate, it required only three weeks to restore their normal male vigor and normal sexual behavior.

Breeding powers have not been linked so commonly with the quality of the feed according as that quality is dependent on the fertility of the soil. Nor have they been connected with protein contents and mineral contents of feeds as controlled by the soil fertility. It is impossible to connect animal fecundity with feed quality dependent on the fertility elements in the soil if those elements do no more than merely increase plant bulk or the carbonaceous character of it. We have long recognized that fattening feeds do not improve, but rather hinder and even destroy, breeding powers. It is not generally recognized that declining soil fertility induces changes in crop compositions: that such decline encourages carbonaceous more than protenaceous properties; and that such changed properties of feed are responsible for lower breeding powers in our domestic animals. Instead, new males are commonly purchased and artificial insemination has been called in for its multiplying power of the male in terms of numbers of females served. We have given repeated emphasis to the fact that the male is half the herd. Such emphasis on one animal as half lets us forget that breeding cannot proceed without the other half, namely the females. This over-emphasis disregards the low fecundity of the poorly nourished females whose failure to produce good egg cells in readiness for conception is not cured by merely plying them with more semen. Such trouble calls for better nutrition of the females in terms of more fertile soils. Reproduction is a matter of good nutrition of both female and male. Neither half can fulfill its share of the performance unless it is well nourished.

Ecology in Terms of Soil Fertility Must Guide Wildlife Management

Unfortunately, the science of soil did not precede the art of farming. Instead the former is following slowly after the latter. The various cropping successes and failures have been helps in building our knowledge of the soil. They served as postmortems to point out where the fundamentals of our soil knowledge can now guide the wiser placement of the crops of plants and like-wise our crops of wildlife. The program of wildlife management in Missouri is going forward on that premise. Wildlife is no longer independent and at the top of the biotic pyramid as it was in the virgin country. It has fallen under man's dictates. It will survive only as we use our information and means to direct wisely the growing of a wildlife crop just as we direct the growing of any other crop. All these crops depend on the soil, and our management of the soil will favor or hinder the wildlife just as it favors or hinders the other crops we desire.

In the ecological pattern of any form of life certain soil areas or regions support it more favorably than others. We have been slow to consider the soil as the factor exercising the favor in terms of the better food it provides. We were prone to magnify the rainfall, the temperature, the cover, as separate factors more than to recognize the soil as it results from the climatic forces and thereby the soil as control of growing the food and the shelter. Now that the soils in lower rainfall are recognized as producers of mineral-rich, proteinaceous feeds we can see why herbivorous feeders like buffalo and cattle grow and reproduce there on the scant prairie vegetation. Then when soils under higher rainfalls and temperatures are of low fertility and produce only forest vegetation we can see another type of wildlife that must be omnivorous and carnivorous. We can understand why such an area is the region for the fattening of cattle more than for growing them. We can understand why the wildlife there is in such grave danger of extinction, expecially when the limited areas of better soil like lowlands are under intensive arable use. If wildlife is to survive the soil must become the basis of wildlife management like it must be for any other crop management.

Soil Pattern of Missouri is the Wildlife Pattern

The significance of the soil is emphasized by the fact that "a single soil type, the Clarksville stony loam, now supports 79 percent of the turkeys in Missouri. This soil, of residual limestone origin, is characteristic of the very rugged and completely dissected parts of the Ozark Plateau. Only 40 percent of it is farmed. The Clarksville gravelly loam in the same soil series supports 15 percent of the turkeys making a total of 94 percent of the birds in the state occurring on these two soil types within a single soil series. With 70 percent of the gravelly loam under cultivation, turkey populations on this second soil type in this series are on the decline".

The soil fertility pattern of Missouri can well be the geographic pattern for wildlife of the state as it is and must be for domestic animal life. This has been demonstrated by feeding trials using lespedeza forage, grown on the five major areas of Missouri, brought to Columbia, and fed to rabbits (Belgain hares). The forage from the different soils grew rabbits with a wide variation in efficiency for a given feeding period. The Grundy soil (Northwest Missouri corn area) produced 637 grams gain; Lintonia (Southeast Missouri lowlands) 561 grams; Eldon (Western Missouri prairies) 505 grams; Clarksville (Ozarks) 420 grams; and Putnam only 316 grams. These soils arrange themselves in this same order, except for the Putnam, when one considers the calcium and the phosphorus of the feed retained in the rabbit body. These figures are the arrangement in order of the relative values of these soils as producers of rabbits. This is not the order in which one might arrange them for agricultural production when topography and other features commonly considered important are used in grouping them. Soils can no longer be classified in terms of productive capacities using bushels or tons per acre as the criterion. We must classify soils, not in terms of fattening power of adult animals, but in terms of a much more critical classification, namely, the capacity to reproduce and grow animals.

More Fertile Soils Mean More Wildlife

The size of the wildlife crop can be taken as an indicator of the productivity of land just as we use a corn crop and say or "this is fifty bushel corn ground." Using Jasper County, Missouri, with the two prominent soil types, Gerald and Cherokee as illustrations, Mr. Wm. D. Shrader of the Federal Bureau of Plant Industry, Soil Survey Division, has taken the data of various wildlife harvests, that is quall, rabbits, opossum, skunk, muskrat, coyote, and mink, in a season and evaluated these two soils in terms of acres needed as support per animal or bird of the wildlife corp. The Gerald soils produced one animal or bird per every 16 acres while the Cherokee produced one such only on 41 acres. Both soil types are similar in most respects as commonly observed, except for the generally accepted higher productivity or more fertility of the Gerald. The wildlife corp confirms this commonly accepted difference. Thus there are plenty of reasons for believing that the soil types of the State of Missouri arranged in order of their fertility or productivity of feeds for domestic animals are likewise an arrangement of them in order of their capacity to give us a crop of wildlife. They suggest then that wildlife management for the production of this crop is premised on the soil fertility in like manner as is the production of feed crops and of our domestic animals.

Summary

In the summary the matter of wildlife management for its production is not much different than the production of domestic animals, except for the advantage of the fact that the former is not handicapped by its enclosure within the farm fences. It can exercise its self-regulatory choice of feed and escape some bad management, even though it is being crowded into more and more restricted territory. The soil fertility is the raw material by which we run a wildlife factory, and the product put out by it is no more numerous and no better in quality than is allowed by the stock of raw material in the soil for growing it. Then, too, our management cannot exert much compulsion since Nature is slow and cannot be readily stampeded. Wildlife must grow and multiply itself in place. It cannot be multiplied by merely transplanting. Exploitation of the crop of wildlife is rapid. Rebuilding and reestablishment are slow Our soil resources have been dwindling rapidly. Their decline has been a powerful force pulling the crop of wildlife down at the same time. Wildlife management must become a party in the great cause of better soil management and in conservation of the soil, since only by that means can wildlife be on secure basis for conserving and rebuilding the object of the hunter's great desire, namely, a good crop of game.

CHAPTER 26

Soil Fertility & Wildlife —Cause & Effect

ALWAYS INTERESTED IN FOOD, the public recently has developed a new, intense interest in the nutritive value of food ingredients. Limited as to the quantity of their food, the consumers are focusing their attention more sharply on the quality of each item, particularly its service in proper nutrition.

Progress in the science of feeding domestic animals is telling us that chemical analyses for carbohydrates, protein, fats, fiber, and minerals are not enough as a measure of over-all values of feeds. Then, too, it must also be granted that the vitamin requisites are not yet fully understood. Much less appreciated is the recently recognized fact that the fertility of the soil growing the forages and grain feeds enters as one of the controls of their nutritive value. In support of the belief in the soil fertility as a determiner of food quality, we are submitting for your consideration the postulate that the ecological array of wildlife may be a reflected picture of the variable value of feeds according to the soil fertility growing them.

When food is the foremost ecological factor, not so much in terms of bulk but rather in terms of nutritive quality, and when the latter is connected more closely with soil fertility than the former, surely we must grant that the soil producing the food plays an important role. We must guard against the belief that wildlife—the same belief is erroneously held too often for our domestic animal life—can thrive well merely because it ingests ample amounts of vegetative bulk. Vegetation may be highly defective in nutrient qualities because of the low fertility of the soil that produces it.

Viewed in a simple way, growth consists of a group of interrelated chemical syntheses, or construction processes starting with the simple chemical elements of the soil and moving into greater chemical complexities through successively dependent life forms. For animal life seventeen of them are essential. For plant life fourteen, at least, must be provided. Four of these constitute about 95 per cent of the body of either animal or plant. These are oxygen, carbon, hydrogen, and nitrogen, representing in the human body, for example, 66.0, 17.5, 10.2, and 2.4 per cent, respectively. They originate in the air and water, hence as widely distributed elements in gaseous and fluid forms their supplies are free-flowing. They are not fixed and do not occur as limited supplies in restricted localities.

In contrast to the four elements of meteorological origin, thirteen elements are demanded from the soil by animal life. Six of these are present in the human body in amounts larger than one-tenth per cent. They are calcium, phosphorus, potassium, sodium, chlorine, and sulfur with 1.6, .9, .4, .3, .3, and .2 per cent, respectively. The remaining seven elements have magnesium at the head of the list amounting to .05 per cent, followed by iron as .004 per cent and then by copper, .00015, manganese, .0003, and iodine, .00004, followed by cobalt and zinc in amounts too small to be accurately specified but nevertheless, essential. In addition to those on the last list of seven for animals, plants require boron not seemingly needed by animals. But plants do not require cobalt, sodium, and chlorine, which are required by animals.

Calcium and phosphorus serve in organic combinations but not so effectively in "salt licks." Calcium and phosphorus are at the head of the list of thirteen elements coming from the soil. They have long been recognized as essential for all life, and have been used extensively as fertilizer applications on the soil for plant production. Their shortages in the soil have been contributory to deficiency diseases and other animal troubles. Calcium in the blood plays a role in the heart rhythm, in the control of muscle tone and in the clotting ability of the blood. Phosphorus is an essential constituent of many important proteins and is integrated with the body mechanisms for making use of energy foods. Calcium and phosphorus, which are closely connected in natural mineral compounds, much as they are in fertilizer service, are closely related in their contributions toward animal requirements when they are deposited in bones and teeth in nearly fixed proportions and are secreted in nearly fixed amounts in milk.

Calcium and phosphorus constitute over 90 per cent of the mineral matter in the body. Most of the calcium, and approximately 80 per cent of the phosphorus, are in the skeleton and serve the obvious function of mechanical support. This function leads to the erroneous concept of their fixity and inactivity. This concept fails to engender an appreciation of the readiness with which they move into and out of the bones in relation to: (a) The supplies in the food, (b) the intake of Vitamin D, and (c) the activity of the particular hormone produced by the parathyroid glands. The additional fact that these two elements combine themselves in varying proportions with hydrogen or other elements as a possible third part in their combinations to form salts and then as combinations with many other elements in colloidal forms, complicates the picture so much that to date the role played in animal life by these two soil-given elements is not extensively charted.

When the calcium and phosphorus as colloidal organic combinations with sugar or with glycerol (e.g. calcium hexosemonophosphate or calcium glycerophosphate) deposit the inorganic calcium phosphate into a richitic bone more effectively than is done by ionic solutions, there is a suggestion that our attention to these two elements in mineral form, or ionic form, has not led us to realize that they may be giving a greater service in animal life when they come from the soil through the plant which synthesizes them into these more beneficial organo-colloidal combinations. Plant synthesis of these soil-given nutrients—calcium and phosphorus—may not only put them into more serviceable colloidal combinations, but it may also package with them some other complexities, like Vitamin D, for example, so that a small amount of these two nutrients in the forms resulting from natural plant synthesis is far more valuable than much larger quantities ingested as salts or other mineral combinations of calcium phosphates. Here is a suggestion that nutrition of wildlife and domestic animal life by working forward from the soil is better than backward from the mineral pile or the drugstore.

What has been said in so much detail about calcium and phosphorus, which are at the head of the list of thirteen soil-given nutrient elements, will readily suggest the possible complexities and importance of the other ten or eleven essential chemical elements coming to food service for wildlife from the same source. When absence or even shortage of any one of these elements can be disastrous, there is still the handicap when any one is not in the most suitable organic combination as a result of failing plant syntheses. The studies of calcium and phosphorus coming from the soil as they control the distribution of wildlife and of domestic life prompt ready consideration of the broader principle that the ecological array of all life—including even man—is a picture of variable nutrition in terms of the soil fertility of the region producing the foods. In other words, life is according to the soil fertility of Mother Earth that nurses it.

That those interested in wildlife should be concerned about the high mortality in the young has its counterpart in the concern by men in animal husbandry about the similar situation in the young of domestic animals. Dr. Ralph Bogart of the College of Agriculture of the University of Missouri passes on the estimate that 40 per cent of the pigs farrowed in Missouri do not live to weaning age. He reports that eight-tenths of the loss, or 32 per cent, of the pigs farrowed occur before they are two weeks old.

That the deficiencies in soil fertility are back of this sad picture has not been generally appreciated. Instead of calling on the agronomists and soil scientists to help stock the soil with calcium, phosphate and other essentials for prevention of this trouble, we are prone to call on the veterinarian for its cure. The fecundity of the female is not a matter of fattening foods of photosynthetic origin in the plant but rather of growth-promoting foods of biosynthetic origin there. One swine producer of Missouri, who gives attention to his feeds as they come from fertile soils for his brood sows, gives a high figure of pigs per litter and such high vigor of them that during the last 3 years each of about 80 brood sows has sent 1739 hogs to the market. His sows have shown less than 25 per cent loss between farrowing and weaning.

The fecundity of the male, too, has been demonstrated by rabbits as dependent on soil fertility when males fed lespedeza hay from soil given phosphate only threatened to become sterile while those fed hay made from the same variety of forage plant grown on soil fertilized with both limestone and phospate remained active in all the respects that mark the virile male as different from one castrated. The significance of the soil fertility as it enables these male rabbits to serve as progenitors of their kind rose decidedly in so short a time as 3 weeks when the hays for the two lots of rabbits were reversed.

Here then is evidence that wildlife as it reproduces and multiplies itself is connected with soil fertility. It is not necessary then to remind you that maternal body growth, foetus development, and birth must each come in full function in presentation of a new body. Body physiology in total of both male and female must be doing well long before reproduction is possible. Reproduction is seemingly the climax of all physiological behaviors. It is the keystone, as it were, between ascendent life activities on one side and decadent life activities on the other. When growth is a constructive performance depending on the soil fertility for its building materials, we ought to see that mating foetus formation, and the development of a body into bone and brawn are much more closely connected with the soil-given elements calcium, phosphorus, and others than is the fattening process that uses carbon hydrogen, and oxygen contributed by water, fresh air, and sunshine.

Perhaps you may not be a soil chemist, but, nevertheless, you will be interested in a brief scan of the rainfall and evaporation of the United States as they illustrate the construction of soils in the western half, exclusive of the Pacific Coast, and the destruction of soil in the eastern half. (Figure 1.)

Soils are a temporary rest stop of rocks enroute to the sea, while being pushed from solids to solution through the agency of water as a solvent and as a transporter. In regions of lower rainfalls, the rocks are broken into small fragments. They are not extensively dissolved and only the more soluble elements, like sodium and potassium, are chemically broken out of the rock minerals. Only a small portion of the rock is decomposed far enough to form clay. Soils are then dominantly sandy. The clay, too, has not become highly stable, nor has it taken on so completely the capacity to

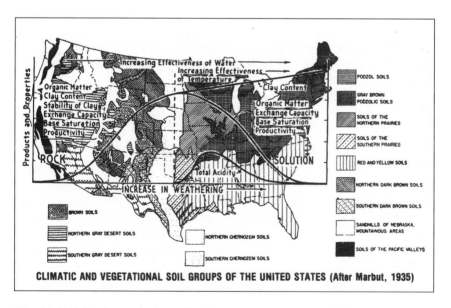

CLIMATIC AND VEGETATIONAL SOIL GROUPS OF THE UNITED STATES (After Marbut, 1935)

Fig. 1—Soil development through all stages, from rock to solution, is illustrated in the United States with the more fertile soils in the Midlands where the bison was common.

hold and exchange nutrients. In fact, it is a clay with properties distinctly characteristic of the low rainfall climate, and associated with soils whose sandy and silty mineral fragments are scarcely different from the parent rocks contributing them.

With increasing amounts of annual rainfall, and especially as these are made more effective by higher temperatures, there is a greater accumulation of clay in the soil. The minerals, too, have not only been more finely broken down, but those more soluble have been leached out and only those more stable and insoluble are left to make the mechanical framework of the soil. The clay has been submitted to more drastic chemical treatment, with the resulting product more stable and more active in holding and exchanging chemical elements including the hydrogen to give it the characteristics of soil acidity.

This increased chemical activity in holding and exchanging positively charged ions is the acme, or top, of soil construction when along with the significant amount of clay and the exchangeable nutrients it carries, there remain in the silt and sand separates of the soil enough minerals other-than-quartz to represent a reserve of plant nutrients to be later broken out for plant nourishment. Such are the soils in the Midlands of the United States, or those in a broad belt extending north and south with approximately the 97th meridian as the central line. The chernozems, or the black and dark prairie soils are distinctly typical of soil construction at the maximum, or soil destruction at the minimum. Here is the great lasting belt of nourishing resources for life in the United States. It is closely delineated by the wheat belt, and, along with the other wheat belts of the world. Emphasizes the small areas that can truly serve as more nutritious food sources of this nation and other nations involved in the world war struggle.

The eastern United States with its higher rainfall, and particularly the Southeastern States with both rainfall and temperature much higher, represent rock breakdown carried more completely toward soil destruction. The mineral particles remaining in the sizes of sand and silt are mainly quartz that contributes nothing to nourishment of life either lower or higher. The clay formed under such intensive weathering is also of a far different mineral and chemical make-up than that with high capacity to hold and exchange other nutrients. Tropical, or red clay, does not hold even the non-nutrient hydrogen. With the reddish color of the clay, there is less activity of holding in exchangeable form those elements of nutritional service as well as of soil acidity. Our southern soils then are not seriously acid, nor can they hold significantly large supplies of calcium, magnesium, potassium, and other nutrients for delivery to the crops, or against leaching by rainfall.

Proteinaccousness vs. Carbonaccousness in the Crops.

Plant growth is initiated by the reserve nutrients held in the seed. It is pushed forward by the fertility contributed by the soil. Plant mass increases as these contributions amounting to about 5 per cent of the plant come from the soil and serve to let the sunshine's energy fabricate carbon dioxide from the air, and water coming via the roots, into the combustible part or the framework of the plant. This synthetic activity by light, or photosynthesis as it is commonly labeled, constructs sugars, starches, lignins, and other carbon compounds, mainly carbohydrates. Their physiological function in animal life is one of providing energy by their chemical breakdown through oxidation. Potassium is a catalytic agent and serves in their photosynthesis, but does not appear in their final form. This process of photosynthesis is the first step in all plant growth. It is readily recognized by the increase in plant bulk and is measured as tonnages per acre. It synthesizes the fuel values of the vegetation to give as fires when it is lignified into wood, but it serves for plant, animal, and human energy when as sugars—or starches converted into such—it plays the main role in the katabolic body processes for energy release.

Because of the emphasis on photosynthesis as a plant performance and the close association of tonnage increase of vegetation with the weather, we have given little or no thought to the synthetic performances carried on within the plant that are not directly prompted by sunshine energy. Animal growth and human body increase occur by their own anabolic activities. Dare we not believe that the plant carries on within itself similar activities whereby it gets energy by burning some compounds as a means to synthesize or construct others into complexities of its own characteristic creation? Cannot plants be more than simply a case of photosynthesis that delivers products of no greater elaboration than lignified cellulose or wood, and of no more value than that of energy delivered by oxidation or burning?

That plants do carry on elaborately complicated performances is attested by the fact that they synthesize the many recently recognized vitamins. These catalysts are still outside of the category of synthesis by animal life, even though by cooperating with the microbes—single celled lower forms of plant life—ruminating animals synthesize over a half dozen of them in their intestinal tract. Humans, too, produce at least one in that portion of our anatomy that is embryologically exterior to the body. Yeasts, that pass their existence in the darkness, and therefore do not indulge in photosynthesis, are significant forces for vitamin synthesis. Such chemical synthesis, may well be called biosynthesis or synthesis by life in contrast to photosynthesis or syntheses by light.

Plants are carrying on these different biosyntheses, however, in magnitudes controlled by the soil fertility and not directly controlled by sunshine and weather as is true for photosynthesis. Here in these biosynthetic activities is the real service performed by plants for higher life. Here is the real control by which soil fertility determines the nutritive value of vegetation for animal and human life. Compounds of biosynthetic origin are not so simple nor plentiful as starches or sugars that are energy compounds. Rather they are the union of carbon, hydrogen and oxygen as basic photosynthetic compounds. Then by consuming a part of them for energy in the process, the nitrogen, phosphorus, sulfur, calcium, magnesium, and all the other soil-borne elements are synthesized into another part of them to give the building blocks and catalytic agents of growth of body rather than agents supplying only fuel. It is this biosynthetic use of soil fertility by plants that gives proteinaceousness, and the host of other possibilities in building and repairing the bodies rather than in providing energy to keep them running. Unless the soil fertility is available plants are mainly photosynthetic and serve the latter function alone. Low supplies of soil fertility can still supply vegetative bulk or produce the factory structure. It requires delivery of soil fertility going through that factory, however, to give seed harvests and services in nourishing growing bodies of higher life. (Figure 2.)

Herbivorous vs. Carnivorous Habits According to Soil Fertility.

The vegetative pattern of the United States as it is helpfully proteinaceous or deficiently carbonaceous determines whether wildlife is herbivorous or carnivorous in its feeding habits. This difference in feeds controlling the kinds of higher life forms is clearly illustrated by the nutritious grasses and other herbages of the western plains; the hard wheat of high mineral and protein contents of the prairies that becomes less so or more starchy and softer on coming eastward; for fattening corn in the eastern extrem-

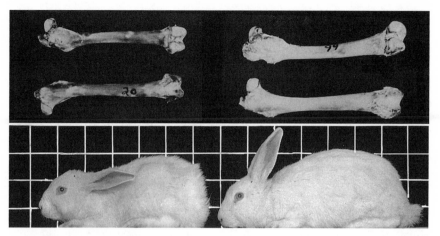

NO TREATMENT   SOIL TREATMENT

Fig. 2—Fertilizer treatments register their beneficial effects in the plant, but more noticeably in the physiology of the animal consuming it, as shown by better weight, wool, bones and other body products and functions. Rabbit and bones on the left record the lack of soil treatment in contrast to the effects of soils treatment on the right for these herbivorous feeders.

ity of the prairies reaching into Illinois; and then the hardwood forests and finally the southern pines or other conifers in eastern and southeastern United States. It is a difficult mental struggle to carry the wildlife and domestic life pattern—to say nothing of human health pattern—across from west to east. With wildlife like the bison subsisting on herbaceous vegetation on the plains area can we not realize that the biosynthetic activities by the plants on those mineral-rich, unleached soils must result in animal diets that are almost complete in nutrient needs even though these are only herbaceous foods? Such diets provide not only energy in carbonaceousness for protective speed, but also calcium, phosphorus, proteins, vitamins, and all other soil-borne essentials and elaborations for muscle, bone, reproduction, and all other body parts and processes for maintenance of the species. When wildlife survival is so closely connected with the soil, certainly the soil fertility must be ample in both kinds and amounts of the dozen chemical essentials for life. It is these same soils on which man lives sufficiently and almost completely on an herbaceous basis by means of hard wheat. Bread from such soil fertility products can really be called the "staff of life."

Higher rainfalls in eastern and southeastern United States present a pattern of different kinds of wildlife, drawing not so directly from the soil the dozen chemical elements needed. More processes, more elaboration and more interventions of different life forms are necessary to collect and pass on all they must have to survive. They are farther removed from the soil in their nutrition when they roost, or run about, in the tree tops. Seeds, as the reproductive insurance effort by the plant and as a smaller part of the whole plant into which there are concentrated the biosynthetic products of a season's collections, are needed for animal survival. The terminal buds into which the soil fertility is concentrated by means of translocation from the lower leaves and limbs of the plants are the only plant parts taken as browse. Animals of herbivorous habits are few per unit area, and then they are characterized by shyness, slender bodies, and high speed, more than by boldness and vigor for fight. It is no stretch of your imagination to supply illustrations of wildlife pointing to contrasts resulting between the more fertile soils of the West and the less fertile soils of the East and South.

Should we carry the wildlife pattern into the much more highly leached soils of the humid tropics, the prominence of carnivorousness of land animals—to say nothing of it for aquatic forms—will immediately emphasize itself. The law of the jungle and its dense tropical forest vegetation has always been "the law of the tooth and the claw." Each life form that survives must use the soil fertility collecting efforts and synthesizing processes of not only plants but also of other animals in assemble and deliver the dozen essential elements in nourishing forms to guarantee its survival. It is only through these circuilous poules of consuming other life forms that the animal reaches over enough territory to provision itself for existence on the soils that are so infertile relative to higher life but seemingly fertile if judged only by tonnages of woody vegetation.

The pattern of life, natural or managed, must fit pattern of soil fertility; paralled then with soil construction and soil destruction as outlined by the increasing forces of rock weathering in Nature, these are the variations in chemical composition of the vegetation from proteinaceousness to mainly carbonaceousness. Likewise there are those wildlife forms and habits that go from the herbivorous to the carnivorous. When this pattern of thinking about wildlife as it can feed itself, is fully understood according to the premise of soil fertility on which it rests, then the places favorable for different kinds of wildlife will be readily recognized as specific locations on the map according to soil fertility. Then, too, the efforts in management of wildlife will not be a matter of political appeasements to payers of hunting license fees by planting wildlife artificially in haunts preferred by the hunters. But rather it will be one of making wildlife natural by feeding it naturally through the soil. It will be one of educating the people to the appreciation of the soil as the basis of all life in terms of soil fertility.

Let us hope that a few of the broader general principles here set forth will stimulate the continued wildlife research to collect more facts and establish still more principles which will make conservation of soil, of wildlife, and of all other life, not the responsibility of professional and employed commissions alone, but the responsibility and privilege of each and every one of us as citizens of a great democratic country.

In Defense of the Cow

A fitting afterword for this volume on forage nutrition is a previously uncited publication by Dr. William A. Albrecht, "In Defense of the Cow." It caps Albrecht's oft-stated dictum that the cow is a better nutritionist than any Ph.D. on the staff.
— Charles Walters

NOW THAT WE are beginning to be more conservation-minded nationally, it was recently well said by Bernard Frank, "Wherever man seeks to improve upon his environment—to increase the productivity of his land and water resources—without adequate knowledge of the ecological mechanisms thereof, his ignorance—even though innocent—is more likely to upset the balance of nature. And whenever man carries this process of improvement to the point of exhaustion of the resources, he must look around for some-·thing on which to put the blame for his folly."

Because man is above the animals and other life forms in the biotic pyramid between him and the soil serving as the foundation of all of them, his failure to fit himself into nature makes him pick on his scapegoats. We are taking the cow as a case in question for this discussion, and are rising as her defense attorney to plead her case.

In view of the above quotation, which summarizes so well our failure to practice conservation of our natural resources, one can see in those remarks the outline for this discussion which divides itself nicely into five sections.

1. *Man's assumption of the natural resources for his exploitation and use while oblivious of their contribution to him through other life forms.*
2. *His inadequate knowledge of ecological arrays, or patterns, of life according as the soils create and nourish them.*

3. *The upset of the balance of nature, by his technologies used according to his economic criteria for improved environment.*
4. *The impending exhaustion of our neglected but vital resources, especially the soil fertility.*
5. *Other life forms paying with their death penalty by taking the blame, as illustrated by our foster mother, the cow.*

The cow, as one of our livestock forms, may well serve in this discussion as the scapegoat for man's folly in aiming to increase the productivity of his land resources without giving consideration to how she and all the other life forms, including man himself, are paying for his folly in not fitting into nature when he believes he is managing and controlling all.

Man Today Assumes the Natural Resources for his Exploitation and Use; But Forgets Their Contributions Through Other Life Forms

Man is of necessity the apex of evolutionary forces. He is also the most complex physiological unit of different life processes. Consequently, he makes the most demands for, and covers most land area in finding the means of satisfying his nutritional requirements. The cow, only one step lower in the evolutionary scale, must also cover much land area in collecting her feed essentials. Primitive man, living closer to nature, and in fuller respect of the cow's instincts for wisely selecting her necessary nourishment, put the cow ahead of the plow. She went ahead and he followed. By her choice of grazing, she was assaying the fertility of the soil according as this grew vegetation which was truly building her a healthy body, reproducing her offspring and thereby multiplying her species. Primitive man followed the cow to outline the agricultural areas of the early world. He was not oblivious to her contribution of essentials for herself in the contributions by plants. She was synthesizing them into still more complicated organic compounds. All of these were supporting primitive man and making possible the many intricate and unknown physiological processes by which he, as a reasoning animal, may have dominion over the rest of them. Primitive man was fitting himself into nature rather than fighting her as his ruler.

Modern man stepped out of the confines of territory outlined by the cow. He disregarded her ability as an assayer of the soil fertility creating her nutrition in terms of proteins, vitamins and mineral elements, all combined into high-quality feed along with carbohydrate bulk. He put the plow ahead of the cow on more lands to conquer. Equipped with newer tools and more power in his command, he moved out of the semi-arid lands. He moved away from the sea shores, out of the cow pastures, and into regions of high rainfall, and high yields of bulk of vegetation.

But he moved into regions of less proteins, where no life forms duplicating his complex physiology, or that of the cow, had ever been known to survive. Did the Pilgrim fathers find any human life form surviving in New England, unless a fish as fertilizer under each hill of corn was used to grow this starchy crop? Did they find cows or other herbivorous feeders scattered in good numbers throughout Virginia and the south to suggest that the soils were growing forage crops giving much of the proteins and these complete enough for fecund animal reproduction? Modern man overran large territories. He expanded his domain. He gloated in the control of it and in his new-won freedom, but he was dragging the cow along in spite of her protest.

The cow, transplanted under such circumstances to the eastern United States, has been in extensive revolt there. She refuses to subscribe to the economics of cheap gains and cheap gallons. She objects to being confined by fences, in spite of tortures by the yokes and barbed wires on going thru them. She goes out on the railroad right of way or highways to be killed by speeding trains, autos, and other death-dealing transports.

In the south, she insists on coming out of the Piney Woods to graze along the very edges of the pavement so persistently that her mangled carcasses on the highway shoulders are not an unusual sight for the motor traveller in the Coastal Plains areas. She is refusing to conceive and to freshen according to our planned schedules. She takes to mastitis on slightest provocation. She is putting bacteria into her milk more commonly. She is not nursing her own calves successfully enough to escape calling in foreign nurse cows. She is taking all kinds of baffling "diseases," ailments and irregularities in her health. She is moving in that direction so badly that killing her to save other cows, and even humans, is threatening her own bovine species with extinction.

The cow, too, enjoyed expansion of her domain and of her freedom on being taken west. That was her bonanza when she arrived in the midcontinent. There the bison had mapped out the soils in his assay of them according as they were regularly helping little buffaloes become big ones and big ones make many more little ones every spring.

But from there she was soon pushed farther west. A grain agriculture replaced her. Suitcase farming, like all extensive, highly mechanical cultures, has always disregarded the cow for her contributions to the good food and good health of man, readily forgetting her as his foster mother. That disregard was provoked by the rush to collect (rather than earn) the most possible from the natural resources. That rush for the resources comes at the cost of their speedy exploitation and not their conservation. While modern man's technologies have lengthened his life lines and lifted his living standards far above those of the primitive, they have shortened and lowered, most seriously, those of the cow.

Moved to the urban pavements now to the extent of more than 90% of our population while but 10% and less of it retains contact with the soil, according to a late census, it is difficult to appreciate the dangerous length to which man's life lines are stretched. Many of them are breaking. Many are being shortened and even cut off. Are we surprised that man, so far removed from the source of his food, and from the experience of his hands working directly in the creation of it, should be a ready victim of crowd psychology, or of communistic promises for collecting a living rather than earning it?

Do the violent swings in election results and the mounting numbers of such swingers not suggest that we are no longer living by democratic principles which classify each of us as independent in our political philosophy, but rather, as we are running hither and yon, take to any kind of belief offering more for less? Can our dwindling natural resources per person as a result of exploitation and increasing population be lessening our faiths in our individual future securities?

Insufficient is our Knowledge of the Physiology of Different Agricultural Plants and Livestock Dominating the Location According as the Soil Fertility Supports Them and Their Output of Created Values

When the cow went west, where she has been doing so well by "rustling" for herself on the range, she was merely reporting that it is the soil and not the particular grass species that supports her in making her calf crops. She is telling us that agriculture will not give an abundant production by our animals merely because of what species of crops we choose.

Rather she is telling us that most abundant production by our animals will be possible only when the soils anywhere offer to any plants the protein-producing, the life-creating potential they offer in the semi-humid soils along the 97th meridian. The cow is revolting against our ignorance of her choice of crops grown on fertile soils delivering body-building rather than fattening values. She is pointing to the soil fertility pattern in control of the different ecological array of plant species, and thereby of all animal species, including even the human.

That any and every soil should provide balanced fertility for any plant which we might choose, seems to be taken for granted. Shall we expect alfalfa, which is famous as a protein supplement, to make its excellent feed values on the same soil where Korean lespedeza accepts broom sedge (*Andropogon virginicus*) as its nurse crop? We turn our crops out in a seeding operation in the spring time and expect them to "rustle" for themselves. At harvest time we go out with combine or picker to round them up and measure the yield, much as the pioneer Ozarker turned the sow out into the woods in the spring and then in the colder fall weather, when sow-belly as supplement to cornpone was needed, took his gun to round up the sow and litter to see the size of the pig crop.

Our knowledge of plant requirements as soil fertility is insufficient to know on what soil to put each crop for the highest yields in both *quantity* and *quality*. Nor do we know just how to feed each crop to make it good feed for the cow, even if with the use of nitrogen we are making hundred bushel corn crops very common occurrences. We call it a crop rotation when we have in succession on the same soil even a 50-bushel corn crop creating 225 pounds of incomplete protein in the grain and then a red clover crop that fails in yielding two tons of forage representing nearly 500 pounds of much more complete protein, and equal to making up the protein deficiencies in corn by serving as a protein supplement for it.

If we haven't yet learned how to keep the same crop growing continuously and successfully on the same soil, why should we believe a collection of four or more crops juggled into a rotation on the same soil should be more wisely, or suitably, nourished to create the collections of widely different nutrient compounds by which each of them grows? Why should there be nutritional virtues in crop juggling because there are more virtues in the rotation in relation to the labor program, or other economic aspects of farm management? Isn't it hight time that we learn just what each crop must be given, via the soil, to feed it for the creastive (not just filling) functions it performs? When we discard certain small grain varieties in favor of new ones because as we say "The old varieties are running out" can't we believe they are running out in search of nourishment just as the cow is doing when she breaks through the pasture fence? Is the case for the hungry crops which are confined to the soils of declining fertility any different from the case of the hungry cow breaking out of the much-farmed, fertility-exhausted pasture to get to the unfarmed and unexploited soil on the highway or railroad right of way?

Crop juggling to get various rotations and juggling out the "tried and true" while juggling in the "new," have been popular agronomic pass-times. We have juggled in the substitutes with no thought of their fertility demands on the soil. Yet we claim high feeding values for the cow from certain crops as if these qualities in the harvest were guaranteed by the pedigree, regardless of what the plant might find in the soil to live up to the claims for it by the seedsman. When reputable crops failed, we searched the world for substitutes. When the substitutes made equal or more bulk they were accepted as of equal value to the cow, compelled to consume them in her struggle to survive. In spite of the deaths from bleeding disasters by cows fed on sweet clover substituting as a legume for red clover, and many other sad disasters for her, our juggling of crops continues to bring in those of less and less feed values on soils under declining fertility levels. Shall we not defend the cow against such ignorance of crop differences in their values as feeds when we do not realize that much crop bulk per acre is no guarantee of correspondingly much true feed value for the dumb beasts unless the fertility of the soil guarantees it?

More recently we have heard much about juggling the cow from one pasture to another through the season in so called "pasture-systems." assuming the cow to be little more than a mowing machine. Can it be good nutrition if she is compelled to take nothing but a non-legume on one soil for two or three months; then nothing but a protein-rich legume in the next phase of this system; and then some other crop, and so on, with no chance to balance her diet daily as she does remarkably skillfully to make more cow, more calf, more milk, and more money for her owner in pastures of mixed herbages on fertile soils? Should we not defend the cow against systems placing her as a live, physiological unit on the level as low as a mechanical grass cutter?

Just as the cow is struggling to find what she requires to grow in her body, so plants are struggling to find in the soil what is required to grow their plant tissues. The problem of protein supplements for the cow points out that she is struggling to find not just "crude proteins" or any organic substance containing nitrogen. Instead she is searching to find the required array of amino acid components of complete proteins to grow her body, to protect her against disease, and to reproduce her kind.

For man, the truly complete proteins must supply him with atleast eight specific amino acids. For the white rat of common experimental use, the completeness of the proteins demands ten different amino acids. For the pig and the chicken these specific requirements have not yet been so completely worked out, but for them the proteins and amino acids of animal origin are still a major safety factor. For the cow the requirements are simpler. She solves her own protein problem if given ample range over young herbage of variety and the cooperative, synthetic helps of the microbial flora in her paunch and intestinal tract. That the synthetic services of the latter transcend those in the intestines of the pig and chicken, is suggested when these last two animals have always taken to the cow's droppings long before the nutritionists believed some vitamin B_{12}, or the so-called "dung factor" (cobalt), passed from the cow for the benefits recognized by the pig or the chicken following her. Our knowledge of just what the soil pattern is by which our livestock is well fed, especially in respect to the proteins, is still much of an unknown. It leaves much to the cow's own selection if she is to be healthy and reproduce readily and regularly.

Our Industrial Rather Than Biological Direction of Agriculture Under Technologies Upset the Balance of Nature

While we commonly boast of our technological knowledge and skills in manufacturing implements, machines, and household gadgets, contributing much to our high standard of living; while that high standard is now about as common out in the country, where things grow, as it is on paved streets, where as the Indian pointed out "Nothing will grow"; and while one man in agriculture can now produce many times more bushels of corn, wheat, oats, etc. than one man produced a quarter century ago; nevertheless, agriculture cannot be viewed wholly as if it were an industry. It may apply industrial principles to the transformation of the products it grows. But the creation of those agricultural products is *not man's, but nature's production.* Life processes in their complexity and their interdependencies are not yet extensively comprehended, much less, are they submitting themselves to man's complete control.

The growing of calves does not lend itself to mass production and assembly line procedures as does, for example, the manufacture of washing machines. Mass production for lowered cost per washing machine is a sound business, economic and industrial principle in case of the latter, but not in the former. Quite contrary to the common concept, the cow herself, and not her owner, or herdsman, is the major director and manger of the calf-producing industry. Materials and machines have let us tabulate their limited properties and behaviors for use in an industry. But even then, our initial design of the washing machine soon revealed its many weaknesses and found so many of its parts out of proportion and out of balance to call for modifications of design about as quickly as the costs of tooling up had been covered.

While some phases of agriculture may be guided by principles used in industry, nevertheless agriculture cannot take its necessary raw materials for granted as available in ordered quantities and at regular costs. Agriculture deals with living, perishable things. These are involved in numerous and uncontrollable interrelations with other living and perishable matters. The growing of calves calls for living cows, and living bulls to create them; healthy milk from healthy cows to nurse them; grass, hay, grains, carbohydrates, proteins, vitamins, trace elements, antibiotics, and a host of possible unknowns to feed and grow them. Calf production is not a case of control of this process by the herdsman. Instead he soon realizes that he is merely an observer and attendant of a business the cow herself is managing and controlling. It is not an industry on her part. She seldom indulges in what even suggests mass production. Quite otherwise, it is biology first. Living cows and calves are always biological processes first and foremost. They may eventually become the raw materials, on their death, for industrial processing in the slaughter house. From that point onward the cow ceases to manage the meat-producing business, and contributes the raw materials for the meat-packaging industry.

Up to this moment much of agriculture, emphasizing the industrial viewpoint and the economics of it, has been slowly upsetting the balance of nature. While those imbalances in many cases represent deficiencies initially unrecognized, they eventually magnify themselves into disasters. Under so much emphasis on industry, with increased output and consumption of resources at a greater rate, the balance of nature is also moving into serious threatening upsets.

Many cases may be cited. Students in wildlife pointing to our exploitation of game have given us many of them. The fox-prairie dog balance is commonly cited. For our discussion here, the imbalances of soil fertility and plant species bringing on the plant species—animal imbalances and the whole series of balances upset by soil exploitation and attempted remedy by fertilizer treatment may well be called up in defending the cow compelled to live under these many former balances of nature we have upset.

Our criterion of agricultural production has been that of weight or volume per acre, per cow or per other producing unit. More weight or volume delivered per animal per unit of time has been considered the economic requisite in animal production. More bushels or tons per acre are praised as agronomic accomplishments. In searching for crops for maximum mass output per acre while taking our soil fertility for granted and exploiting it, we have brought in those crop plants producing mainly carbohydrates, or photosynthetic bulk, but a lowered concentration within that vegetative mass of the proteins, vitamins, inorganic requisites and other nutrient essentials. Production of much vegetative mass, but less of seed per unit of that weight, encouraged the belief that a grain-producing agriculture is poor economy and a grass agriculture should be substituted for it.

Hybrid corn has been an excellent illustration when the crude protein concentration of that pre-hybrid grain as a mean of 10.3% some 30 years ago, has dropped to a low of half that during the last three or four decades in the United States. These figures tell us nothing about the nutritional quality of the protein, particularly the deficiency of certain amino acids to the point of demanding protein supplements to corn even for fattening services by this grain. Here, literally, a new plant species was brought in, pushing out an older one as either the vegetative production went up or the soil fertility went down. Nature's balance is being upset slowly but decisively.

In our increasing carbohydrate production—which is also a case of decreasing protein synthesis—naturally the animal-plant balance is upset. Animal fattening and all the speculation connected with buying low and selling high has become the major phase of what we call animal husbandry. Hybrid corn and the soils under it, even if put to other crops, have not been the regions for growing calves even though they are the areas for fattening them. They are the regions for hogs, made up as their bodies are largely of fats, or of converted carbohydrates. They are the regions where animal diseases prevail, and those diseases apt to be considered contagious rather than degenerative or deficiency ailments, because so many animals are so often in contact.

The introduction of the high-yielding fescues for lush, late-season grazing and hay is too much bulk and so little nutrition for health that it often invited the lameness of a swollen rear ankle, called "fescue foot," curiously, it strikes the left hind foot first and the animal's extended lameness offers little hope for profitable recovery, much like the once-considered highly contagious "hoof and mouth" disease.

The cow-plant species balance of nature is so badly upset that we are now pushing animal populations to smaller figures, even if the cow population is at this moment relatively high. It is slowly dawning on us that fattened animals are not healthy animals, at least not in a condition which is healthy for the species. One needs only see the fattening geese in Strasburg, France, where American corn is fed them until fatty degeneration of the liver makes that organ the desired delicacy of the slaughtered goose while the rest of her body is scarcely considered for food purposes, to make us realize that fattening our castrated cattle does not improve their health or the chances for survival of the species. Can agriculture as a biological procedure, long maintain itself when nature's balances are so seriously upset that they eliminate the animals that give us our major foods in the proteins?

Other illustrations of imbalance may be cited, like our campaign on what we call "weeds" coming in as competitors to other crops. Are we not "fighting" weeds because we fail to have enough fertility by which the desired crop would dominate the area so thoroughly that the weeds would not be competitors? Shall we not consider weeds as plants making so much woody bulk on so little fertility that they survive where crops demanding much fertility for little but highly nutritious bulk cannot dominate them? In our fight on weeds with herbicides, we are scattering the deadly carbon-ring compounds in chlorinated and sulfonated arrangements so profusely that not only plants, but microbes, animals and even man are confronted with dangers to health and even with death. Such upsets in Nature's balances are the result of the changed combinations of fertility of the soil not generally considered as the determiner of agriculture itself. Once we upset them, then, like Humpty Dumpty, they cannot be put back together again.

The Gradual Exhaustion of Our Creative Resource, Viz, the Fertility of the Soil, Goes Unheeded While Our Livestock Suffers

Our efforts to increase productivity of the land have slowly come to consider the soil as the point where the major effort must be applied to serve. Unfortunately, so much soil has already been exhausted before we come to the realization of the soil as the starting point of the assembly lines of agricultural production. National propaganda for soil conservation that started with gullies, has finally arrived at consideration of conservation and restoration of soil fertility where gullies start.

The need to put fertility back into the soil was first appreciated in the south, where bird guano from South America was one of the early fertilizers. Clearing of piney woods by the colonial pioneer in the south gave rainfall, fresh air, blue sky, and sunshine, but no significant fertility for extended crop production. There was soil organic matter originating in pine needles, but this didn't release much fertility on cultivation. Nor did the soils of the south have much mineral reserves of fertility to improve the land by "resting" it. No unweathered minerals are washed in by the rivers, if the delta is excluded. No windblown additions of high fertility come in as is true for Missouri, Iowa, Nebraska, Kansas, and other states with "loessial" soils. No unweathered subsoils are turned up by the plow or are within root-reach. The soil fertility was already seriously exhausted from the soils of the south when the Creator managed the place and could do no better than create pine wood, and little or no protein to support even a timber squirrel.

Because of that climatic setting, attention went to feeding the crop plants with fertilizer intensively and extensively. That was necessary on those nearly lateritic soils, which are not only low in fertility but so low also in their adsorption and exchange capacities that they would not even become seriously sour or acid. They will not hold much applied, soluble fertilizers, and let much go out in drainage waters for loss of economic returns from this salvage effort. With no serious acidity, the needs by the crops for calcium and magnesium were neglected, save for the calcium applied in ordinary super phosphate and possibly some magnesium used unwittingly for the correction of fertilizer acidity.

Sulfur too was highly exhausted from the soils of the south but applied unwittingly with benefit through mixed fertilizers made up mainly of super phosphate, carrying about half as calcium sulfate. This element suggests its serious exhaustion from, or serious deficiency in, the soils of the South if one dares to conclude from the fact that peanuts, a significant food legume of the south, provide protein but one so low in the sulfur-containing amino acid, methionine, to require protein supplements of it when fed. Might we not see other legumes also deficient in feeding potential for the same reason?

Other elements, particularly the trace elements, may also be highly exhausted in the soils. Their use for citrus crop improvement, and on peat soils, raises the point seriously whether we must not view our soils more and more as being feedlots for our crops if these plants are to synthesize feed values rising above those represented by pine needles. Must we not see more and more soil fertility exhaustion giving us crops that may be supplying only bulk but not necessarily proteins, vitamins, mineral elements and all that is truly animal feed?

Can this vision of the soil help us believe that carbohydrate crops of starch, oils, and cellulosic fiber dominate the ecological pattern, because of these deficiencies in soils highly weathered under much rainfall and high temperatures? Even cotton seed protein will not supplement corn for pigs or chickens, but will for the cow where the paunch seems to overcome the handicap of this protein supplement for animals not symbiotically propagating a similar internal bacterial flora.

Now that we have taken thirty million acres out of growing horse feed and turned them over to cattle; that sheep at the maximum of numbers in 1942 are now at the lowest since we began counting them; and that hogs are also less now than formerly but yet cattle have not increased to the extent that decrease of horses would suggest; isn't it time for someone to rise in defense of the cow as the symbol of our livestock on the decline? Is not the declining soil as declining feed quality possibly causally conneted with livestock troubles? Cannot increasing livestock troubles and failing health be due to failing quality of feed and that due to failing soils? Can our crop juggling and disregard of exhaustion of fertility have finally brought the nutritional values of forages and feeds so low that what we call cattle "diseases" is no more than failing cow physiology because she can stand up under those deficiencies no longer?

Our Livestock is Taking the Blame and Paying the Penalty While we Fail to Defend the Cow

One needs only to take a long range view of what is happening at the marketplace and im commerce to see signs and suggestions over the long range. Beef has risen in price to tell us that the supply is short in relation to demand, but is taken even at the unusually high prices. Producers of hogs are talking about shifting this former mortgage lifter by means of fat to more of a protein producer by means of its lean muscle.

Can beef that once grew itself in the western U.S. now be dwindling there where high protein wheat is rapidly becoming soft, starchy wheat because of soil fertility exhaustion? Why are hogs being pushed westward and away from grain to more grazing on alfalfa in the plan for their growing more muscle cheaply in place of excessive fat? Have not beef cattle markets travelled westward so rapidly across the United States to locate themselves in Kansas City, St. Joseph, and Springfield, Missouri, and Omaha, Nebraska, because that is where the beef was making itself as the cow selecting the soils determined it more than any diversified farming plans of ours would have it? Isn't it out on the range where the less weathered soils and high protein forage really *grow* the cattle while on the highly weathered soils of the East we only *fatten* them?

When our pastures fail in their fertility required for the nutritious forages they still produce many plants we call "weeds." We say "The weeds took the pasture" and then start a "war on weeds." We fail to realize that the plants we call "weeds" are merely those which can make much bulk on the low fertility where the desired forage could not. Weeds grow prominently in the pasture because they are not making enough feed values to tempt a cow to eat them. In place of defending the cow's judgment of the low nutritional value of the so-called "weeds" and her report thereby of the soil fertility in the pasture that needs rejuvenation, we fight the weeds with mowing machinery and more recently with the dangerous and deadly poisons. Isn't it time that such judgment of the forage and of the soil fertility by the cow that transcends our own be defended?

Now that drugs and poisons not only for fighting weeds, but for fighting insects and microbes are demonstrating their dangerous side reactions as well as supposedly beneficial main reactions, it is essential that we consider the animal as a complex physiology more than as a piece of property. With chlorinated naphthalenes finally connected casually with Keratosis, virus X or other baffling ailments, it seems well that we see our failure to protect and to nourish our cows as responsible for many of the troubles for which we blame and even kill the dumb beast.

When in the state of Missouri the calf crop at weaning time was only 60% of the conceptions before artificial insemination was used, and now is of no larger percentage figure when artificial insemination is such a common practice, has the scattering of noble pedigrees by this artificial technique done anything to increase the species? Is the increasing legislation against disease, and are the increasing indictments of sales barns not suggesting that the animals are not protecting themselves as they once did? If we keep on killing sick cows to protect those we have not yet examined or detected, will our cow population increase, and can the producer take the shock of the loss of his herd that suddenly shows positive to some possibly questionable test when on the proceeding inspection a clean bill of health was given?

Epilogue

Now that our once-specialized barn-feeding technique of such high repute not so long ago is failing to serve, we are suddenly going to a grass agriculture. Is this because out of desperation from our failure in feeding the cow, we are turning that responsibility over to the cow herself? If so, it is relatively late in the experience, now that our soils are so low in fertility that they must be kept in grass cover to keep them from eroding, for us to expect the cow to give us a market for the quality of grass that is no more than just soil cover. If we are finding the soil fertility too low to create other crops than grass with economic returns, isn't it foolhardy to believe the shift to grass a way of getting more creative services via an animal on such a high physiological level as that of our foster mother? Shall we not look at the grass agriculture as the last desperate crop juggling act, when grass by its dense root system has more soil fertility extracting power than other crops, and thereby a maximum of survival under direct circumstances? Will we not finally turn to putting fertility into the soil to feed our crops with some measure of what is needed for plant nutrition just as we try to feed ourselves according to standards of good nutrition? Only when we feed our crops properly by correctly treating the soil with applied soil fertility and restored soil organic matter, will we initiate the processes which can carry the synthesis of feeds and nutritional values from the soil up through the plants to the animals and to man for the benefit of all these life forms in good nutrition, in good health and in fecund reproduction. Only by such condition will creation work in the fullest sense.

Only by considering all life forms in balance, and by viewing the ecological patterns of microbes, plants and animals in relation to the soil fertility that creates them, can we wisely direct our agriculture, and modify our environment or improve upon it for greater productivity. The cow as man's foster mother has brought him out of his primitivity and helped him design his technologies for his high standards of living. By means of those he has taken to exploiting his environment with the disregard of the cow, and against her continued protests. She has outlined the ecological patterns for herself and delineated the soils on which she and man could primitively survive. Displaced as she is, she is no longer able to defend herself and is slowly going down in defeat. She is being killed because she gets sick, and is being turned upon by man for whom she has been foster mother. Are you as a jury going to decide against her, or are you not going to vote for her acquittal and for fertile soils under her and thereby under you and the generations you procreate? You as the jury must decide.

BIBLIOGRAPHY

Microbiological Assays of Hays for Their Amino Acids According to Soil Types and Treatments, Including Trace Elements.

1. Association of Official Agricultural Chemists. Official and Tentative Methods of Analysis of the Association of Official Agricultural Chemists. Menasha, Wis.: George Banta Publishing Company. Ed. 6, 1945.
2. Marais, J. S. C., and Smuts, D. B., The amino acid deficiencies of certain plant proteins and the supplementary effect between plant proteins as measured by means of biological values. Onderstepoort Jour. Vet. Sci. Animal Ind., 15: 225–238, 1940.
3. Harrow, Benjamin, Textbook of Biochemistry. Philadelphia: W. B. Saunders Company. 1941, (p. 117.).
4. Stokes, J. L., and Gunness, M., Microbiological method for determination of amino acids I; aspartic acid and serine. Jour. Biol. Chem., 157: 51–59, 1945.
5. Stokes, J. L., and Gunness, M., Dwyer, I. M., and Caswell, M. C., Microbiological methods for the determination of amino acids II; a uniform assay procedure for the ten essential amino acids. Jour. Biol. Chem., 160: 35–49, 1945.

Discrimination in Food Selection by Animals.

1. Richter, Curt P., 1942–43. Total self-regulator functions in animals and human begins. The Harvey Lecture Series, 38: 63–103.
2. Mitchell H. A., and Hosley. N. W., 1936. Differential browsing by deer on plots variously fertilizers. Black Rock Forest Paper I. 24–27.
3. Price, Weston A., 1943. The role of a new vitamin–like activator in the control of dental caries. Jour. Amer. Dental Assn., 30: 888–905.
4. Evans, E. A. Jr., et al. 1942. The biological action of vitamins. A Symposium. Riboflavin—Paul Gyorg p. 61. University of Chicago Press.

The Influence of Soil Mineral Elements on Animal Nutrition.

1. Albrecht, Wm. A., and Klemme, A. W., Limestone mobilizes phosphate into Korean lespedeza. Jour. Amer. Soc. Agron. 31: 284–286, 1939.
2. Albrecht, Wm. A., Potassium in the soil colloid complex and potassium nutrition. Soil Sci., 55: 13–21, 1943.
3. Albrecht, Wm. A., Protein Deficiencies via Soil Deficiencies. H. Experimental Evidence. Oral Surgery, Oral Medicine and Oral Pathology, 5: 483–499, 1952.
4. Bonner, James and Arthur W. Galston, Principles of Plant Physiology. W. H. Freeman & Company, San Francisco.
5. Browne, Charles E., A Source Book of Agricultural Chemistry. Chronica Botanica, Waltham, Mass.
6. Broyer, T. C., Carlton, A. B., Johnson, C. M., and Stout, P. R., Chlorine. A micronutrient element for higher plants. Plant Physiology, 29: 526–632, 1954.
7. Corrie, F. W., Some Elements of Plants and Animals. The mineral elements of plant and animal nutrition. Fertilizer Journal, Ltd., London, 1948.
8. Graham, E. R., Testing Missouri Soils. Mo. Agr. Expt. Sta. Cir. 345, 1950.
9. Horner, Glenn, Relation of the Degree of Base Saturation of a Colloidal Clay by Calcium to the Growth, Nodulation and Composition of Soybeans. Mo. Agr. Expt. Sta. Res. Bul. 232, 1935.
10. Kochler, Fred E. and Albrecht, Wm. A., Biosynthesis of amino acids according to soil fertility. III. Bioassays of forage and grain fertilized with "trace" elements. Plant and Soil, IV: 336–344, 1953.
11. Marshall, C. E., The activities of cations held by soil colloids and the chemical environment of plant roots. "Mineral Nutrition of Plants," Chapter 3, Univ. of Wisconsin Press, 1951.
12. Pfander, W. H., Muhrer, M. E., Brooks, C. C., and Garner, G. B., Rumenology. Research for Better Farm Living Mo. Agr. Expt. Sta. Bull. 619, 1954.
13. Reed, Lester W., Biosynthesis in Plants as Influenced by Inorganic Nutrient Balance in the Soil. Ph. D., Thesis Univ. of Missouri, 1953.
14. Schroeder, R. A., and Albrecht, Wm. A., Plant Nutrition and the Hydrogen Ion. III. Soil calcium and the oxalate content of spinach. Bul. Torrey Bot. Club. 69: 561–568, 1942.
15. Sheldon, V. L., Blue, Wm. G., and Albrecht, Wm. A., Biosynthesis of amino acids according to soil fertility. I. Tryptophane in forage crops. Plant and Soil I: 33–40, 1951.
16. Sheldon, V. L., Blue Wm. G., and Albrecht, Wm. A., Biosynthesis of amino acids according to soil fertility. II. Methionine contents of plants and sulfur applied. Plant and Soil II: 361–365, 1951.
17. Steen, Melvin O., Not How Much, but How Good. Missouri Conservationist 16: 1–3, 1955.

18. Walton, Izaak, The Complete Angler, p. 109. Everyman's Library. J. M. Dent & Co., London.

19. Wittwer, S. H., Schroeder R. A., and Albrecht, Wm. A., Vegetable crops in relation to soil fertility. II. Vitamin C and nitrogen fertilizers. Soil Sci. 59: 329–336, 1945.

20. Wittwer, S. H., Albrecht Wm. A., and Goff, H. R., Vegetable crops in relation to soil fertility. III, Oxalate content and nitrogen fertilizers. Food Research 11: 54–60, 1946.

Feed Efficiency in Terms of Biological Assay of Soil Treatments.

1. Albrecht, Wm. A., and Smith, G. E., Biological assays of soil fertility. Soil Sci. Soc. Amer. Proc., 6: 252–258, 1942.

2. Auchter, E. C., The interrelation of soils and plant, animal, and human nutrition. Science, 89: 421–427, 1939.

3. Crampton, E. W., and Finlayson, D. A., Pasture studies: VII. The effect of fertilization on the nutritive value of pasture grass. Emp. Jour. Exp. Agr. 3: 331–345, 1935.

4. Crampton, E. W., and Forshaw, R. P., The interseasonal changes in the nutritive value of pasture herbage. Sci. Agr., 19: 701–711, 1939.

5. Crampton, E. W., and Maynard, L. A., The relation of cellulose and lignin content to the nutritive value of animal feeds. Jour. Nutr., 15: 383–395, 1938.

6. Hester, Jackson B., Influence of soil fertility on the quality of tomatoes. Soil Sci. Soc. Amer. Proc., 6: 343–345, 1942.

7. Schuphan, W., Eine kritische Stellungnahme von Agrikulturechemie and Medizin zur Frage der alleinigen Stallmistdungung bei Gemuse. Die Ernahrung, 5: 29–42, 1940.

8. Stubblefield, F. M., and DeTurk, E. C., The composition of corn, oats, and wheat as influenced by soil treatment, seasonal conditions and growth. Soil Sci. Soc. Amer. Proc., 5: 120–124, 1941.

9. Vandecaveye, S. C., Effect of soil type and fertilizer treatments on the chemical composition of certain forages and small grain. Soil Sci. Soc. Amer. Proc., 5: 107–119, 1941.

10. Williams, Dorothy E., MacLeod, Florence L., and Morrell, Elsie, Availability to white rats of phosphorus in lespedeza sericea and alfalfa hays. Jour. Nutr., 19: 251–262, 1940.

11. Williams, Dorothy E., MacLeod, Florence L., and Morrell, Elsie, Availability to white rats of phosphorus in soybean and red clover hays. Jour. Nutr., 20: 391–398, 1940.

Biosynthesis of Amino Acids According to Soil Fertility, III: Bioassay of Forage and Grain Fertilized with "Trace" Elements.

1. Albrecht, Wm. A., and Smith, G. E., Biological Assays of Soil Fertility. Soil Sci. Soc. Am. Proc. 6, 252–258 (1941).

2. Kendall, K. A., Nevens, W. RB., and Overman, O. R., The Lactation Response as Limited by Feeds Produced Under Two Systems of Soil Fertilization. J. Nutr. 36, 625–638 (1948).
3. McLean, E. O., Smith, G. E., and Albrecht, Wm. A., Biological Assays of some soil types under treatment. Soil Sci. Soc. Am. Proc. 8, 282–286 (1944).
4. Rose, W. C., Half–century of amino acid investigation. Chem. Eng. News 20, 2385–2388 (1952).
5. Sheldon, V. C., Blue, Wm. G., and Albrecht, Wm. A., Diversity of amino acids in legumes according to soil fertility. Science 108, 426–428 (1943).
6. Sheldon, V. C., Blue, Wm. G., and Albrecht, Wm. A., Diversity of amino acids in legumes according to soil fertility. II. Methionine content of plants and the sulfur applied. Plant and Soil 3, 361–365 (1951).
7. Sheldon, V. C., Blue, Wm. G., and Albrecht, Wm. A., Biosynthesis of amino acids according to soil fertility. I. Tryptophane in forage crops. Plant and Soil 3, 33–40 (1951).
8. Smith, G. R., and Albrecht, Wm. A., Feed efficiency in terms of biological assays of soil treatments. Soil Sci. Soc Am. Proc. 7, 322–330 (1942).

Biosynthesis of Amino Acids According to Soil Fertility: IV. Timothy Hay Grown with Trace Elements.

1. Albrecht, Wm. A., Trace elements and agriculture production. J. Applied Nutrition VIII, 352–354 (1955).
2. Albrecht, Wm. A., Trace elements and the production of proteins. J. Applied Nutrition X, 534–543 (1957).
3. Albrecht, Wm. A., Pettit Gay, Lee, and Jones, G. S., Trace elements, Allergies and Soil Deficiencies. J. Applied Nutrition XIII, 20–32 (1960).
4. Garner, George B. et al., Learn to live with nitrates. Missouri Agr. Expt. Sta. Bull. 708 (1958).
5. Hampton H. E., and Albrecht, Wm. A., Nodulation modifies nutrient intake from colloidal clay by soybeans. Soil Sci. Soc. Am. Proc. 8, 234–237 (1944).
6. Hogan, A. G., Albrecht, Wm. A., and Norwood, Geo, Value of timothy hay as sheep feed in response to soil treatment. Missouri Agr. Expt. Sta. Bull. 444, 80 (Annual Report) (1942).
7. Koehler, Fred and Albrecht, Wm. A., Biosynthesis of amino acids according to soil fertility. I Tryptophane in Forage Crops. Plant and Soil iii. 33–40 (1951).
8. Sheldon, V. L., Blue, Wm. G., and Albrecht, Wm. A., Biosynthesis of amino acids according to soil fertility. I Tryptophane in Forage Crops. Plant and Soil III, 33–40 (1951).
9. Sheldon, V. L., Blue, Wm. G., and Albrecht, Wm. A., Biosynthesis of amino acids according to soil fertility. II Methionine content of plant and sulphur applied. Plant and Soil III, 361–365 (1951).

10. Stokes, J. L., Gunnes, M., Dwyer, I. M., and Caswell, M. C., Microbiological methods for determination of amino acids. J. Biol. Chemistry, 160, 35–49 (1945).
11. Wendel, Wilmer J., Bioassay of soil fertility under forages via selections and growth by weaning rabbits. Thesis for Masters Degree, Univ. of Missouri (1959).
12. What's New in Food and Drug Research. Biochemists Exploring for Metals. No. 29, January, 1962, Food and Drug Research Laboratories, Maurice Ave, at 58th St. Maspeth 78, New York City (1962).

Soil Fertility and Wildlife—Cause and Effect.

1. Albrecht, W. A., 1943. Soil and Livestock. The Land 2: 298–305.
2. Bogart, Lotta Jean, 1943. Nutrition and physical fitness. W. B. Saunders and Company.
3. Bogart, Ralph, 1944. Loss of pigs. Mo. Agr. Exp. Sta. Farm News Service 32, No. 26.
4. Powell, Elmer B., 1944. Private correspondence.

Publisher's Note:

This bibliography contains reference works that Dr. William A. Albrecht used for research when working on many of the papers contained in this book. Some selections are not available from works that have been obtained from Dr. Albrecht's personal papers.

Index

Also from Acres U.S.A.

ALBRECHT'S FOUNDATION CONCEPTS

William A. Albrecht, Ph.D. After many years, *The Albrecht Papers Vol. 1* is back in print. Nature gave up her rare secrets to Dr. Albrecht simply because he was a curious farm boy who liked logic and adventure. Through his extensive experiments with growing plants, soils and their effect on animals, he sustained his theory and observation that a declining soil fertility, due to a lack of organic material, major elements, and trace minerals — or a marked imbalance in these nutrients — was responsible for poor crops and in turn for pathological conditions in animals fed deficient feeds from soils. These papers addressed to scientists, and especially to farmers who worked with nature are as valid today as when they were first written. *Softcover, 515 pages.*

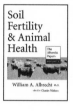

SOIL FERTILITY & ANIMAL HEALTH

William A. Albrecht, Ph.D. Albrecht was the premier soil scientist and was dismayed by the rapid chemicalization of farming that followed WWII. This book, subtitled *The Albrecht Papers Vol. 2* is a well-organized explanation of the relationship between soil fertility and animal and human health. This is a great book for those just familiarizing themselves with these concepts and the perfect companion to Eco-Farm. *Softcover, 192 pages.*

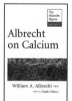

ALBRECHT ON CALCIUM

William A. Albrecht, Ph.D. This valuable collection of essays reveals the insights of a brilliant soil scientist ahead of his time. In this Vol. 5, readers will find a carefully organized and convincing explanation of the relationship between calcium and soil fertility. It is not possible to discuss calcium, which Albrecht proclaims as the "King of Nutrients" without being led into the entire mosaic that Albrecht considers biologically correct farming. Albrecht's work provides an indispensable foundation for anyone interested in sustainable, ecologically responsible agriculture — his teachings are more critical today than ever. *Softcover, 320 pages.*

THE OTHER SIDE OF THE FENCE – HISTORIC DVD

William A. Albrecht. In this 1950s-era film, Professor Albrecht's enduring message is preserved and presented for future generations. With introductory and closing remarks by *Acres U.S.A.* founder Charles Walters, Prof. Albrecht explains the high cost of inadequate and imbalanced soil fertility and how that "dumb animal," the cow, always knows which plant is the healthier, even though we humans don't see a difference with our eyes. A period film, dated in style but timeless in message. Perfect for a group gathering. *DVD format, 26 minutes.*

ECO-FARM — AN ACRES U.S.A. PRIMER

Charles Walters. In this book, eco-agriculture is explained — from the tiniest molecular building blocks to managing the soil — in terminology that not only makes the subject easy to learn, but vibrantly alive. Sections on NP&K, cation exchange capacity, composting, Brix, soil life, and more! *Eco-Farm* truly delivers a complete education in soils, crops, and weed and insect control. This should be the first book read by everyone beginning in eco-agriculture . . . and the most shop-worn book on the shelf of the most experienced. *Softcover, 476 pages. ISBN 978-0-911311-74-7*

WEEDS — CONTROL WITHOUT POISONS

Charles Walters. For a thorough understanding of the conditions that produce certain weeds, you simply can't find a better source than this one — certainly not one as entertaining, as full of anecdotes and homespun common sense. It contains a lifetime of collected wisdom that teaches us how to understand and thereby control the growth of countless weed species, as well as why there is an absolute necessity for a more holistic, eco-centered perspective in agriculture today. Contains specifics on a hundred weeds, why they grow, what soil conditions spur them on or stop them, what they say about your soil, and how to control them without the obscene presence of poisons, all cross-referenced by scientific and various common names, and a new pictorial glossary. *Softcover, 352 pages. ISBN 978-0-911311-58-7*

SCIENCE IN AGRICULTURE

Arden B. Andersen, Ph.D., D.O. By ignoring the truth, ag-chemical enthusiasts are able to claim that pesticides and herbicides are necessary to feed the world. But science points out that low-to-mediocre crop production, weed, disease, and insect pressures are all symptoms of nutritional imbalances and inadequacies in the soil. The progressive farmer who knows this can grow bountiful, disease- and pest-free commodities without the use of toxic chemicals. A concise recap of the main schools of thought that make up eco-agriculture — all clearly explained. Both farmer and professional consultant will benefit from this important work. *Softcover, 376 pages. ISBN 978-0-911311-35-8*

HANDS-ON AGRONOMY

Neal Kinsey & Charles Walters. The soil is more than just a substrate that anchors crops in place. An ecologically balanced soil system is essential for maintaining healthy crops. This is a comprehensive manual on soil management. The "whats and whys" of micronutrients, earthworms, soil drainage, tilth, soil structure and organic matter are explained in detail. Kinsey shows us how working with the soil produces healthier crops with a higher yield. True hands-on advice that consultants charge thousands for every day. Revised, third edition. *Softcover, 352 pages. ISBN 978-0-911311-59-4*

To order call 1-800-355-5313
or order online at www.acresusa.com